NHS handbook

2012/13

The essential guide to the new NHS

Peter Davies

The thirteenth edition of *The NHS handbook*.

First, second, third, fourth, fifth, sixth, seventh, eighth, ninth (then called The Pocket Guide), tenth, eleventh and twelfth editions published by:

NHS Confederation
29 Bressenden Place
London SW1E 5DD
Tel: 020 7074 3200
Fax: 0844 774 4319

To order further copies of this handbook or other Confederation publications, contact our publications sales team on 0870 444 5841 or visit www.nhsconfed.org/publications

978-1-85947-194-4

Printed in the UK in May 2012. The information included is correct at time of print.

Design by Grade Design Consultants, London
www.gradedesign.com

POC00701

This publication has been manufactured using paper produced under the FSC Chain of Custody. It is printed using vegetable-based inks and low VOC processes by a printer employing the ISO14001 environmental accreditation.

Contents

Please contact us on 0870 444 5841 for more information about the versions of *The NHS handbook* 2012/13 suitable for those with a visual impairment.

Sponsor's foreword

 At a time of great change for the NHS, it is reassuring to know that organisations like the NHS Confederation are striving to bring clarity to the healthcare arena. *The NHS handbook* is an invaluable resource, designed to help sift through the jargon and bring clarity to those seeking to navigate the rapidly changing NHS landscape. We are delighted to be sponsoring it this year.

While the new NHS takes shape, one thing is certain to remain constant – the imperative to increase efficiency, ensuring increasingly scarce funds are directed toward those in need. This will always be a priority and that's why at the core of our philosophy is a dedication to providing the best possible value to the trusts with whom we work in partnership.

Another constant is the need for good people. Regardless of changing structures and new chains of command, a quality health service will always need excellent staff. Patients care first and foremost about their need to be treated by staff who adhere to the highest professional standards; who are reliable, caring and compassionate. Any feelings about the reforms are secondary. That's why NHS Professionals works across all staff groups to ensure that partner trusts are always supplied with people of the highest standard; from cooks to consultants and porters to paediatricians.

Despite all the changes to the NHS, people will always be what matter most.

Stephen Dangerfield
Chief executive
NHS Professionals
www.nhsp.co.uk
NHS Professionals
NHS Professionals
@nhsworkforce

Foreword

The NHS has changed so significantly in recent years that the traditional model of NHS care is, in many cases, no longer recognisable. Our healthcare system is more fluid and diverse than ever before and the NHS needs to continually adapt to meet the changing needs and expectations of patients and taxpayers.

The NHS handbook 2012/13 is the must-have guide to help you navigate and make sense of the changing shape of the NHS. With the Government's Health and Social Care Bill receiving royal assent in spring 2012, we have updated the guide to cover:
• the structure of the NHS
• clinical commissioning groups
• the changing provider landscape
• the NHS Commissioning Board
• health and wellbeing boards.

There's also a handy acronym buster to help you find your way around the names of the new organisations, which is also available online at
www.nhsconfed.org/nhshandbook

The NHS handbook is supported by advertising from a number of organisations we work alongside, and I am particularly grateful to NHS Professionals for kindly agreeing to support this landmark edition.

I hope you find this timely guide invaluable in 2012/13. At the NHS Confederation we will continue our work to join up the views, perspectives and opinions of each and every part of the healthcare system over the coming year. If you have any comments or suggestions for future editions of *The NHS handbook*, please contact our publications team on 020 7074 3200 or email **publications@nhsconfed.org**

Mike Farrar CBE
Chief executive
NHS Confederation

NHS CONFEDERATION

Who we are

The NHS Confederation represents all organisations that commission and provide NHS services.

We are the only membership body to bring together and speak on behalf of the whole of the NHS.

We have offices in England, Wales (the Welsh NHS Confederation) and Northern Ireland (Northern Ireland Confederation for Health and Social Care) and provide a subscription service for NHS organisations in Scotland.

What we do

We work with our members and health and social care partners to help the NHS guarantee high standards of care for patients and best value for taxpayers by:

- making sense of the whole health system
- influencing health policy
- supporting our members to share and implement best practice
- delivering industry-wide support functions such as the NHS Employers organisation and the NHS European Office.

We represent the NHS as a whole and have a range of networks and forums to support our members on issues of specific concern to their part of the NHS.

Ambulance Service Network • Primary Care Trust Network • NHS Partners Network • Mental Health Network • Community Health Services Forum

We also offer the opportunity for organisations working across the wider health and social care industry to be a part of the NHS Confederation as associate partners.

Further information

To find out more about the NHS Confederation, please visit our website at www.nhsconfed.org

Introduction

One system – four structures

The National Health Service is based on common principles throughout the four constituent parts of the United Kingdom, although its structure in each is quite distinctive – and increasingly so. Ever since the NHS's foundation more than 60 years ago, it has adapted its shape to the particular administrative and geographical conditions of England, Scotland, Wales and Northern Ireland. But since devolution in 1999, and the transfer of responsibility for healthcare in Scotland, Wales and Northern Ireland to the Scottish Parliament, Welsh Assembly and the Northern Ireland Assembly, the divergence in structure has become more marked. The NHS has also pursued different priorities in each of the four countries.

UK population (2010)

	MILLION	% OF TOTAL
England	52.23	83.8
Scotland	5.22	8.4
Wales	3.00	4.9
Northern Ireland	1.79	2.9
Total	**62.24**	**100**

Source: Office for National Statistics

However, the service's underlying values remain the same. These originate from the 1944 white paper, *A national health service*, which stated that:

> The Government want to ensure that in future every man, woman and child can rely on getting all the advice and treatment and care they may need in matters of personal health; that what they shall get shall be the best medical and other facilities available; that their getting these shall not depend on whether they can pay for them or any other factor irrelevant to the real need.

Both society and the health service have altered almost beyond recognition since then, but the NHS still strives to provide a broadly comprehensive service, mostly free to all at the point of need. As the NHS Constitution, devised in 2008 for the health service in England, expresses it: 'Everyone counts. We use our resources for the benefit of the whole community, and make sure nobody is excluded or left behind.'

Of course, the NHS has had to move with the times to take advantage of scientific and technological advances, as well as political, social and economic change. Major reform programmes have been under way in all four parts of the UK for most of the past decade, although certain principles remain common to all four systems: for example, the NHS provides a comprehensive service available to all and access to services is based on clinical need, not ability to pay.

What the NHS does

Across the UK, the NHS employs 1.75 million staff, 1.35 million of them in the English NHS. Just under half are clinically qualified. The NHS deals on average with 1 million patients every 36 hours. In a typical year, people in England visit GP practices 300 million times, make 19 million visits to accident and emergency departments and almost 5 million calls to NHS Direct. There are more than 4 million ordinary and day case admissions to hospital, and more than 45 million outpatient appointments.

What the NHS does: contacts per day (thousands)

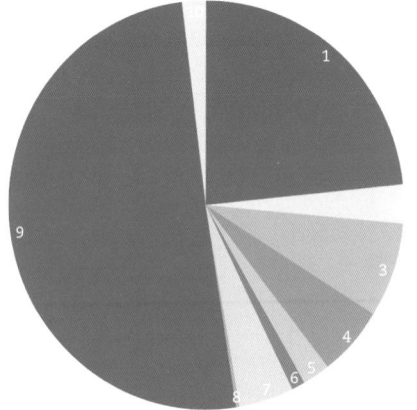

1 Total community contacts: 389 (24%)
2 A&E attendances: 49 (3%)
3 Outpatient attendances: 124 (7%)
4 In bed as emergency admission to hospital: 94 (6%)
5 In bed as elective admission to hospital: 36 (2%)
6 NHS Direct calls: 18 (1%)
7 Courses of NHS dental treatments for adults: 73 (4%)
8 Walk-in centres: 6
9 GP or practice nurse consultations: 836 (51%)
10 NHS sight tests: 28 (2%)

Figures are for England only.
Source: Department of Health

01 The new structure of the NHS in England

The coalition Government's first health white paper, *Equity and excellence: liberating the NHS* (see page 107), was published two months after the 2010 general election and proposed far-reaching structural reorganisation while reinforcing the market's role in England's health service. It declared: 'The current architecture of the health system has developed piecemeal, involves duplication, and is unwieldy', and promised a 'radical simplification' that would 'remove layers of management' while 'putting power in the hands of patients and clinicians'.

New organisations are being established, some existing ones abolished and others are being modified. Under the previous structure, strategic health authorities (SHAs) had acted as the regional headquarters of the NHS since their creation in 2002. Originally 28 in number, they were reduced to ten in 2006. The 151 primary care trusts (PCTs) – reconfigured from 303 in 2006 – were the cornerstone of the NHS locally, and were responsible for 80 per cent of the NHS budget. Both SHAs and PCTs are now in the process of abolition (for transitional arrangements, see page 30).

These developments have been described as representing potentially the most significant change in the NHS's history. They were incorporated into the Health and Social Care Act 2012.

Ultimate responsibility for the NHS remains with Parliament. At a strategic level, the Department of Health will pass much of its day-to-day responsibility to the new NHS Commissioning Board. At an operational level, clinical commissioning groups will occupy a pivotal position in taking decisions about local NHS services. Foundation trusts, care providers, independent and third sector healthcare organisations will continue to provide them. A chain of accountability therefore still runs from local bodies up to Government and Parliament, although there will be a less direct management line.

Parliament

As the NHS will continue to be financed mainly through taxation it will rely as before on Parliament for funds, and must account to it for their use. Parliament scrutinises the service through debates, MPs' questions to ministers and select committees. These procedures mean that the Government has to publicly explain and defend its policies for the NHS in England. The Scottish Parliament (page 210), the Welsh Assembly (page 222) and the Northern Ireland Assembly (page 232) are responsible for oversight of the NHS in their parts of the UK. Health services in the Isle of Man and the Channel Islands are not part of the NHS.

The new NHS structure

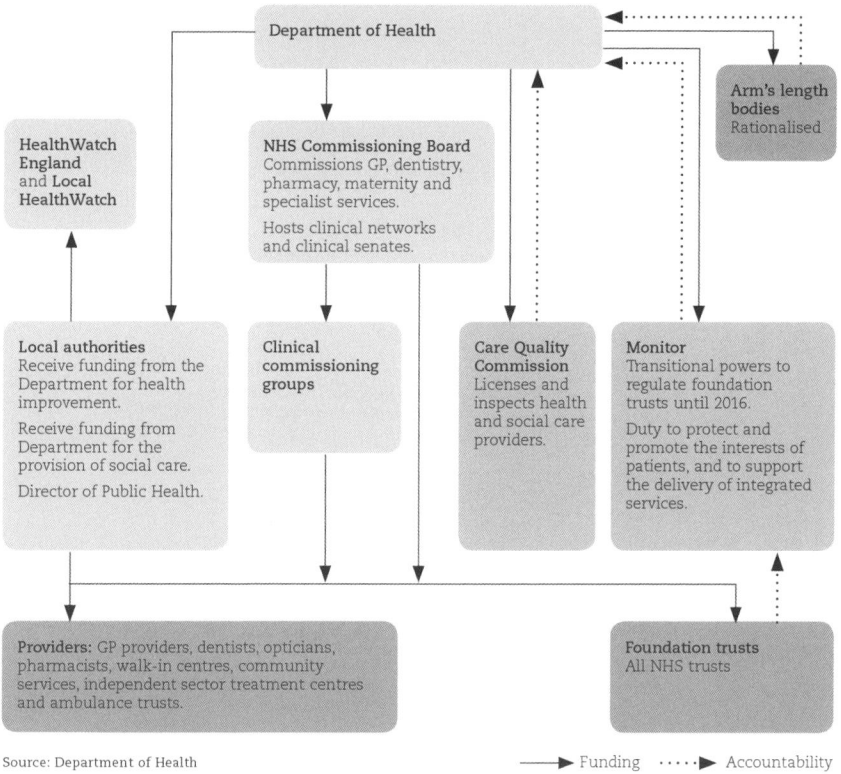

Department of Health

Arm's length bodies Rationalised

HealthWatch England and Local HealthWatch

NHS Commissioning Board
Commissions GP, dentistry, pharmacy, maternity and specialist services.

Hosts clinical networks and clinical senates.

Local authorities
Receive funding from the Department for health improvement.

Receive funding from Department for the provision of social care.

Director of Public Health.

Clinical commissioning groups

Care Quality Commission
Licenses and inspects health and social care providers.

Monitor
Transitional powers to regulate foundation trusts until 2016.

Duty to protect and promote the interests of patients, and to support the delivery of integrated services.

Providers: GP providers, dentists, opticians, pharmacists, walk-in centres, community services, independent sector treatment centres and ambulance trusts.

Foundation trusts
All NHS trusts

Source: Department of Health ────► Funding ·····► Accountability

Role of the Secretary of State and health ministers

Currently five ministers, all appointed by the Prime Minister to the Department of Health, are responsible in Parliament for health and social care. They provide the DH with political leadership and are responsible for deciding strategy and policy, and for agreeing overall resource levels with the Chancellor and the Prime Minister, as well as priorities for distributing resources, based on the strategy and policy framework.

The DH's ministers comprise the Secretary of State, two ministers of state – one responsible for health, the other for care services – and two parliamentary under-secretaries of state, one of whom is responsible for public health while the other sits in the House of Lords. The Secretary of State is a member of the cabinet and has overall responsibility for NHS and social care delivery, system reforms, finance, resources and strategic communications.

The Secretary of State retains an overarching duty to promote a comprehensive health service – a founding principle of the NHS – and will have new duties to promote quality improvement and reduce inequalities. But ministers will not be responsible for providing or commissioning services directly, passing this duty to new bodies such as the NHS Commissioning Board by way of a 'Mandate' (see page 18). The Government believes that previous statutory arrangements 'allowed the Secretary of State a large amount of discretion to micromanage parts of the NHS', and wants to 'liberate the NHS from excessive bureaucratic and political control'.

Select committees

Three select committees, each comprising backbench MPs representing the major parties, are particularly relevant to the NHS. They are all able to summon ministers, civil servants and NHS employees to give oral or written evidence to their inquiries, usually in public. Their reports are published throughout the parliamentary session.

Health committee

The health committee's role is 'to examine the expenditure, administration and policy of the Department of Health and its associated bodies'. The committee now also exercises on Parliament's behalf the power nominally held by the Privy Council to hold the General Medical Council (see page 153) to account, and has extended this to include the Nursing and Midwifery Council (see page 153). In addition, it plans to hold regular annual review meetings with the Care Quality Commission (see page 147) and Monitor (see page 148). The committee has a maximum of 11 members.
www.parliament.uk

Public accounts committee

The public accounts committee scrutinises all public spending and is concerned with ensuring the NHS is operating with economy, efficiency and effectiveness. Its inquiries are based on reports about the service's 'value for money', produced by the Comptroller and Auditor General, who heads the National Audit Office (see page 149). It aims to draw lessons from past successes and failures that can be applied to future activity. The committee has 16 members, and is traditionally chaired by an Opposition MP.
www.parliament.uk
www.nao.gov.uk

Public administration committee

The public administration committee examines reports from the Parliamentary and Health Service Ombudsman (see page 144).
Its remit now includes responsibility for scrutinising third sector policy.
It has 11 members.
www.parliament.uk
www.ombudsman.org.uk

Department of Health

The Government intends to fundamentally change the DH's role. It will no longer be the headquarters of the NHS nor directly manage any NHS organisations. Its main responsibilities will include:

- setting national policy on health and adult social care and maintaining legislation
- setting strategy and outcomes for health and adult social care
- providing leadership
- managing relationships throughout the health and care system
- securing resources and accounting for them
- speaking for the UK on international health issues.

The DH will have strategic responsibility for new and existing bodies, including:

- NHS Commissioning Board (see page 18)
- Monitor (see page 148)
- Care Quality Commission (see page 147)
- Public Health England (see page 46)
- Health Education England (see page 176)
- NHS Trust Development Authority (see page 25).

The Scottish Government Health and Social Care Directorates (page 211), the Welsh Department for Health, Social Services and Children (page 223) and Northern Ireland's Department of Health, Social Services and Public Safety (page 233) provide strategic leadership for the NHS in their parts of the UK. However, the DH has UK-wide responsibility for international and European Union business and for:

- coordinating plans to cope with a flu pandemic
- licensing and safety of medicines and medical devices
- ethical issues such as abortion and embryology.

Managing the DH

The DH is to be streamlined from 13 directorates into five, comprising:
• NHS
• adult social care
• public health
• partnerships and engagement
• operations.

Its two most senior staff, of equal rank, are the permanent secretary and the chief medical officer. These posts are not political appointments and do not change with a change of government. The permanent secretary is responsible for running the department day to day and is its chief accounting officer. The DH's chief medical officer is the UK Government's principal medical adviser and the professional head of all medical staff in England (there are also CMOs for Scotland, Wales and Northern Ireland).

The DH plans to introduce the role of director of nursing, focused on public health. The CMO and director of nursing will be the main source of clinical advice to ministers and the DH. The role of chief nursing officer will be relocated from the DH to the NHS Commissioning Board. Other DH chief professional officers, who provide expert knowledge in specialist health and social care disciplines to ministers and other government departments, are:
• chief dental officer
• chief health professions officer
• chief pharmaceutical officer
• chief scientific officer.

National clinical directors

National clinical directors are clinical specialists and figureheads for specific national service frameworks or clinical strategies (see page 121). They represent the interests of the NHS and social care within the DH. Their most important role is spearheading change by engaging with professionals and providing leadership. The clinical directors number almost 30, and:
• visit health and social care practitioners
• chair taskforces with health and social care professionals and health service managers
• work with the Royal Colleges to ensure changes in health and social care are reflected in training and education
• chair taskforces to develop national clinical strategies, bringing together health professionals, service users and carers, health service managers, partner agencies and other advocates.

Further information
Business plan 2011–2015, DH, July 2011.
Department of Health annual report and accounts 2010–11, TSO, September 2011.
www.dh.gov.uk

Other government departments

A number of other government departments – apart from the DH – have responsibilities that impinge on health, and work in partnership with the NHS. They include:

- **Department for Communities and Local Government:** responsible for housing, regional and local government.
  www.communities.gov.uk
- **Home Office:** lead responsibility for progress on the drug strategy; also responsible for alcohol policy and licensing.
  www.homeoffice.gov.uk/drugs
- **Department for Education:** responsible for children's social care policy, it runs the Healthy Schools programme jointly with the DH.
  www.education.gov.uk
- **Department for Environment, Food and Rural Affairs:** responsibilities include water, farming, fisheries, horticulture and some aspects of rural health and wellbeing. Protection from the effects of pollution or toxic chemicals are particular concerns.
  www.defra.gov.uk

Arm's-length bodies

An arm's-length body is an organisation working at national level, but at 'arm's length' from the DH. They have existed since the NHS was set up in 1948. As stand-alone organisations, ALBs work closely with the local NHS, social care services and other ALBs to carry out specific functions. They vary in size but normally have boards, employ staff and publish accounts. They are accountable to the DH and sometimes directly to Parliament. Most receive substantial funding from the DH.

They include special health authorities, executive agencies and non-departmental public bodies, which are set up when ministers want independent advice without direct influence from Whitehall departments.

Their roles are:
- regulating the health and social care system and workforce
- establishing national standards and protecting patients and the public
- providing central services to the NHS.

After a review of the 18 ALBs that existed when the Government came to power, it has abolished six and moved two others out of the sector. It has also created some new ones.

Further information
Liberating the NHS: report of the arm's-length bodies review, DH, July 2010.

NHS Commissioning Board

The NHS Commissioning Board will be a pivotal part of the NHS's new structure. It will provide leadership for commissioning (see page 38) and will be nationally accountable for the outcomes the NHS achieves. In 2013/14 the Board will have overall responsibility for a budget of £86 billion, of which it will allocate £65 billion directly to clinical commissioning groups (CCGs) (see page 20).

The white paper, *Liberating the NHS*, promised that the Board would be 'a lean and expert organisation, free from day-to-day political interference, with a commissioning model that draws from best international practice', adding that: 'It will not manage providers or be the NHS headquarters'.

After consultation with HealthWatch England (see page 139), the Secretary of State will set the Board a formal Mandate lasting three years, specifying all the Government's requirements and expectations for the NHS. Ministers will be able to make any necessary changes to the Mandate annually. The Board must produce an annual business plan detailing how it intends to achieve the objectives in the Mandate, and report on its performance at the end of the year. As an independent arm's-length body, the Board will also be directly accountable to Parliament.

Its main functions will include:
- developing and overseeing a comprehensive system of CCGs responsible for commissioning most healthcare services
- commissioning directly about £20 billion of services that CCGs will not be responsible for, such as primary care and specialised services (see page 39)
- overseeing the commissioning budget and ensuring value for money
- developing commissioning guidance, standard contracts, pricing mechanisms and information standards
- agreeing and achieving improved outcomes

The Board and its key relationships

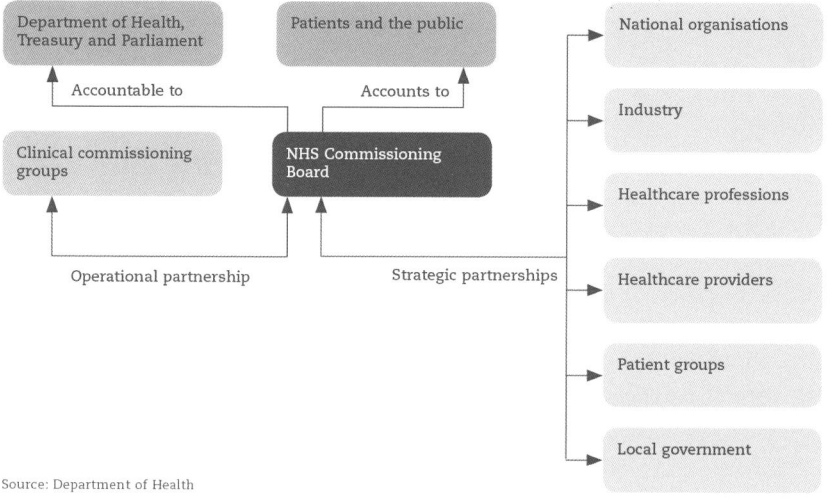

Source: Department of Health

- improving quality by promoting consistent national standards
- promoting innovative ways to integrate care
- reducing inequalities and promoting equality and diversity
- engaging public, patients and carers, championing their interests and ensuring wider access to information
- fostering choice, and with Monitor developing guidance on how choice and competition can be applied to particular services
- overseeing emergency planning
- with its partners, developing a medium-term strategy for the NHS.

The Board's senior team will comprise:
- chief executive
- medical director
- chief nursing officer
- chief operating officer
- national director – commissioning development
- national director – finance
- national director – patient insight
- national director – improvement and transformation
- national director – policy, corporate development and partnership
- chief of staff.

It will have 3,500 staff, two-thirds deployed locally managing relationships with CCGs and performing direct commissioning through 44 local offices. In addition, regional sector offices will cover London, the South, North and Midlands and East. The Board's headquarters will be in Leeds, and it will have a small presence in London. Its budget for running costs in 2014/15 will be £492 million – about half of what is currently spent by the strategic health authorities and other organisations on the same functions.

The Board has operated in shadow form as a special health authority since October 2011. It will be established as an independent statutory body in October 2012, and will be fully operational by April 2013.

Further information
Developing the NHS Commissioning Board, DH, July 2011.
Developing the NHS Commissioning Board – update, DH, October 2011.
Framework agreement between the Department of Health and the NHS Commissioning Board Authority, NHSCB/DH, January 2012.
www.commissioningboard.nhs.uk

Clinical commissioning groups

From April 2013 CCGs will replace primary care trusts as the local NHS bodies responsible for deciding what services are needed and for ensuring they are provided appropriately (for the transition arrangements, see page 30). CCGs were initially called GP commissioning consortia, but the Government recognised that while GPs have a central role in coordinating patient care, commissioning needs to involve a wider range of healthcare professionals.

Using budgets allocated by the NHS Commissioning Board, CCGs will commission services across a range of clinical areas (see page 35), including hospital services and mental healthcare, but they will not commission primary care nor national or regional specialised services, which will be part of the NHS Commissioning Board's remit.

Every GP practice in England will have to belong to a CCG, but beyond certain requirements (see page 136), CCGs will be free to decide their governing bodies' membership, organisational form and their own priorities, taking account of guidance and legislation. However, they will be required to meet in public and publish minutes, as well as details of contracts with health services.

The Government has avoided stipulating what size population a CCG
should cover. The NHS Commissioning Board may vary a CCG's
membership or geographic area to ensure all GP practices are members or
that there is comprehensive geographic coverage, though CCG boundaries
should not normally cross those of local authorities without clear
justification. CCGs are expected to have a name that uses the 'NHS' brand
and is clearly linked to their locality.

The Board has drawn up six criteria that CCGs must satisfy before it will
authorise them. These include 'a strong clinical and multi-professional
focus', meaningful engagement with patients and public, clear plans and
'great leaders who individually and collectively can make a real
difference'. The Board can intervene to support CCGs if they appear not
to be meeting their statutory duties or are at significant risk of failing to
do so. In the event of significant failure, it can dissolve a CCG, subject
to consultation.

The NHS Confederation provides a wide range of resources to help CCGs
develop local commissioning plans and structures, and to influence
national health policy on commissioning (see box above).

Further information
Clinical commissioning group authorisation: Draft guide for applicants, DH, April 2012.
NHS Confederation support for clinical commissioning groups, NHS Confederation,
November 2011.
Developing clinical commissioning groups: towards authorisation, DH, September 2011.
Managing conflicts of interest in clinical commissioning groups, NHS Confederation/Royal
College of General Practitioners, September 2011.
www.nhsconfed.org/ccg

Clinical networks and senates

Clinical networks and clinical senates will exist to advise commissioners in CCGs and the NHS Commissioning Board. They will be hosted by the NHS Commissioning Board.

Clinical networks are not statutory bodies but partnerships of all organisations and professionals involved in commissioning, planning and providing a particular service in a geographical area. They have the potential to break down barriers between primary, secondary and tertiary care and between health and social care. They are particularly well developed in cancer care, where 34 networks throughout the UK each serve 1 to 2 million people.

Clinical senates will enable doctors, nurses and other professionals to jointly take an overview of health and healthcare locally and provide expert support and advice on how different services can best fit together. They should include public health specialists and social care experts.

Health and wellbeing boards

Every upper-tier local authority is creating a health and wellbeing board (HWB) to act as a forum for local commissioners across the NHS, social care, public health and other services. HWBs will aim to develop a shared understanding of local need, develop joint local priorities and encourage commissioners to work in a more integrated, 'joined-up' manner.

Their main functions will be:
- assessing the local population's needs and leading the joint strategic needs assessment (see page 40)
- promoting integration and partnership across an area – for example, by promoting joined-up commissioning plans across the NHS, social care and public health
- supporting joint commissioning and pooled budget arrangements
- scrutinising major service redesign.

HWBs are intended to give local authorities influence over NHS commissioning, and corresponding influence for NHS commissioners on public health and social care. They will have a statutory duty to involve users and the public. The Government hopes that by involving democratically elected representatives and patient representatives it will strengthen the democratic legitimacy of commissioning decisions, as well as providing a forum for challenge, discussion and involving local people.

Membership of HWBs will include:
- at least one councillor
- director of adult social services
- director of children's services
- director of public health
- local HealthWatch representative
- a representative of each relevant CCG
- others the local authority or HWB may choose.

Local authorities will decide for themselves the number of councillors on an HWB, and can insist they are a majority.

The NHS Commissioning Board must take the HWB's views into account in its annual assessment of a CCG, and consult it on the CCG's contribution to achieving the joint health and wellbeing strategy.

Further information
Liberating the NHS: increasing democratic legitimacy in health, DH, July 2010.
Operating principles for health and wellbeing boards: laying the foundations for healthier places, NHS Confederation and partners, October 2011.

Foundation trusts

Foundation trusts run hospitals, specialist care centres, mental health, community health and ambulance services. First established in 2004, they are independent public benefit organisations, modelled on cooperatives and mutual societies, but remain part of the NHS. They are still accountable to Parliament, but local people have a say in running them by becoming members or governors (see page 135). Monitor, the independent regulator of foundation trusts (see page 148), has powers to intervene in how a trust is run if it fails to meet standards or breaches its terms of authorisation. The Care Quality Commission (see page 147) is responsible for inspecting the performance of foundation trusts.

Foundation trust status bestows more freedoms on organisations than they had as NHS trusts. These include:
- the ability to retain any operating surpluses – for example, from land sales – and access to capital from both the public and private sectors; the amount a foundation trust can borrow is determined by a formula based on its ability to repay the loan, and governed by the prudential borrowing code set by Monitor

- a new power to earn up to 49 per cent of their income from treating private patients, though foundation trusts must publish separate accounts for NHS and private-funded services
- an obligation to achieve national standards like the rest of the NHS, but freedom to decide how they do this
- powers to establish private companies
- the ability to vary staff pay from nationally agreed terms and conditions.

By the end of 2011 there were 141 foundation trusts. Of the remaining NHS trusts, the DH had identified 112 as candidates for foundation trust status. These comprised:
- 68 acute trusts
- 19 community service trusts
- 17 mental health trusts
- eight ambulance trusts.

All but one NHS trust in the North East has become a foundation trust, but only 38 per cent in London have done so. The Government wants the 112 NHS trusts either to achieve foundation trust status by 2014, to be merged or taken over or to have their services dispersed; one has already found a private sector partner.

The National Audit Office found that many NHS trusts need to tackle financial, quality and governance issues before they can expect to attain foundation status. It reported that 48 were unlikely to meet Monitor's tests of financial viability. At least 20 – half of them in London – face such deep-seated and longstanding problems, including size and location, that they are not financially or clinically viable in their current form.

Foundation trusts have always been unique to the NHS in England, while NHS trusts were abolished in Scotland in 2004. Wales abolished trusts in 2009, except for its ambulance service, Public Health Wales and another trust providing specialist cancer services, while Northern Ireland reduced its 18 trusts to five in 2007.

Key organisation: Foundation Trust Network

The Foundation Trust Network is the trade association for NHS foundation trusts and NHS trusts on the journey to FT. The network speaks on behalf of over 200 members delivering acute, specialist, mental health, ambulance, and community services in hospitals, in the community and at home. Its role is to ensure the voice of public providers of healthcare in the NHS is heard loud and clear, to support members to deliver excellent patient care and to forge relationships across the whole of the health and social care system.

www.foundationtrustnetwork.org

NHS Trust Development Authority

The NTDA will be established as a special health authority in shadow form in October 2012, and from April 2013 take on full responsibility for NHS trusts seeking foundation trust status. As well as managing the 'FT pipeline', this will include managing performance and intervening in poorly performing trusts. It will have an estimated 120 to 150 staff, and its main base will be in Leeds with an additional presence in London. The need for the NTDA will be reviewed in 2016.

Further information

Achievement of foundation trust status by NHS hospital trusts, NAO, October 2011.
Achievement of foundation trust status by NHS hospital trusts: sixtieth report of session 2010–12, House of Commons public accounts committee, December 2011.
Building the NHS Trust Development Authority, NHS, January 2012.

Independent providers

By using independent providers – private sector companies, voluntary organisations and social enterprises – to offer care to NHS patients, the health service has been able to expand capacity and improve choice. The previous Labour Government introduced this policy in 2002, believing that competition would prompt the NHS to improve its response to patients' needs, and extended it in 2008. The coalition Government is extending it further.

Its policy of enabling 'any qualified provider' (AQP) to offer services to NHS patients will apply to a broader range of care than the routine elective procedures already included. Beginning with a limited set of community and mental health services in 2012, the AQP policy will be implemented in phases and focus on services where patients say they want more choice.

Subjecting services such as accident and emergency (A&E) and critical care to AQP will never be practical or in patients' interests, but elsewhere the Government expects it will improve quality and access, help tackle inequalities and encourage innovation.

To qualify, providers must:
- be registered with the Care Quality Commission and (from 2013) be licensed by Monitor (see page 151) or meet equivalent assurance requirements
- meet the terms and conditions of the NHS standard contract (see page 37), which involves abiding by the NHS Constitution (see page 112), relevant guidance and law
- accept NHS prices
- guarantee to meet agreed service requirements and comply with referral protocols.

Currently, independent sector involvement (excluding GP practices, dentistry and mental health) in the NHS remains static at about 5 per cent of mainstream clinical services. This includes 3.5 per cent of elective care procedures, including diagnostic services.

Care Quality Commission figures show that 96 per cent of NHS patients using independent facilities for elective surgery rate their care favourably, compared to 79 per cent using NHS facilities. Research has shown the public has little concern about who provides care as long as it is of high quality and free at the point of use.

Further information
Operational guidance to the NHS: extending patient choice of provider, DH, July 2011.
Discussion paper 10: Any qualified provider, NHS Confederation/NHSPN, July 2011.
Briefing: A positive partnership – the independent sector and the NHS, NHS Confederation/ NHS Partners Network, October 2011.
AQP Resource Centre **www.supply2health.nhs.uk**

The private sector
Traditionally, private healthcare providers in the UK tended to concentrate on secondary care, but new entrants to the market in the past decade have looked for opportunities in primary and community care too. They have also become major suppliers of diagnostic services to the NHS.

Purchase of NHS treatment from non-NHS bodies 2009/10

1 Independent sector treatment
   centres (ISTCs): 373,058
2 Other private sector: 3,765,513
3 Voluntary sector: 560,445
4 Other (including local
   authorities): 2,749,109
   Total: 7,448,125

Source: Hansard, 28 February 2011

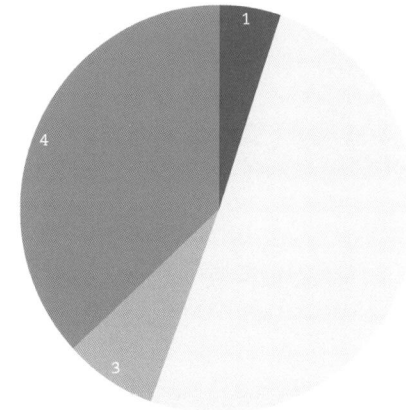

Procedures undertaken by independent sector treatment centres (ISTCs) 2006–10

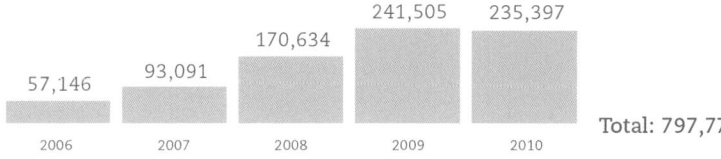

| 57,146 | 93,091 | 170,634 | 241,505 | 235,397 | |
| 2006 | 2007 | 2008 | 2009 | 2010 | Total: 797,773 |

Source: Hansard, 19 July 2011

The previous Labour Government initially encouraged private sector companies to set up treatment centres (see page 83) to carry out elective surgery and diagnostic tests for NHS patients under five-year contracts, to help alleviate waiting times. This paved the way for them gradually to play a bigger role, and volumes of services they provide to the NHS rose rapidly.

The first independent sector treatment centre (ISTC) contracts paid more than the standard NHS rates and guaranteed revenue regardless of activity volumes. Fewer patients than contracted for were treated, leading to 'overpayments' of £252 million. However, as these contracts have been re-tendered at the end of their initial five-year terms, new contracts have contained no such guarantees, leaving only a few still operating on the original basis for the remainder of their contract periods. Average utilisation rates have now risen to 97 per cent.

NHS Partners Network

The NHS Partners Network (NHSPN) represents a wide range of independent sector providers of NHS services ranging through acute, diagnostic, primary and community care. Its members are drawn from the 'for profit' and the 'not for profit' sectors and include large international hospital groups and small specialist providers. The network was established in 2005 and became part of the NHS Confederation in 2007. It champions the independent sector's role in supporting the NHS, helping the drive for quality, integration and efficiency and putting patients first. www.nhsconfed.org/nhspn

Voluntary, community and social enterprise sector

Often referred to as the 'third sector', the range of institutions that fall between the public and private sectors are seen as a key part of the coalition Government's 'Big Society' initiative. Sometimes referred to as 'civil society organisations', they include small local community and voluntary groups, trusts, large and small registered charities, foundations, cooperatives and social enterprises. Third sector organisations have been particularly involved in the provision of mental health services, sexual health services, drug rehabilitation and palliative care. Many smaller voluntary organisations play a crucial part in community services, particularly for vulnerable and excluded groups, and are often able to bridge divides between statutory services. The aim of current policy is that they should become 'equal players' in providing services.

DH research in 2007 found 35,000 such organisations provided health or social care, and another 1,600 planned to do so. Total funding for these services amounted to £12 billion a year, with just over half from the public sector – 36 per cent of which was for healthcare and 62 per cent for social care.

The DH launched a 'voluntary sector strategic partner programme' in 2009 to improve communication with the sector and enable it to work in partnership with the NHS and social care. It now has 18 members drawn from national voluntary organisations, through which the DH estimates it can reach 300,000 organisations across the sector. The DH's voluntary sector investment programme totalled £18 million in 2011/12.

Vital statistics: NHS spending on non-NHS providers (£ million)

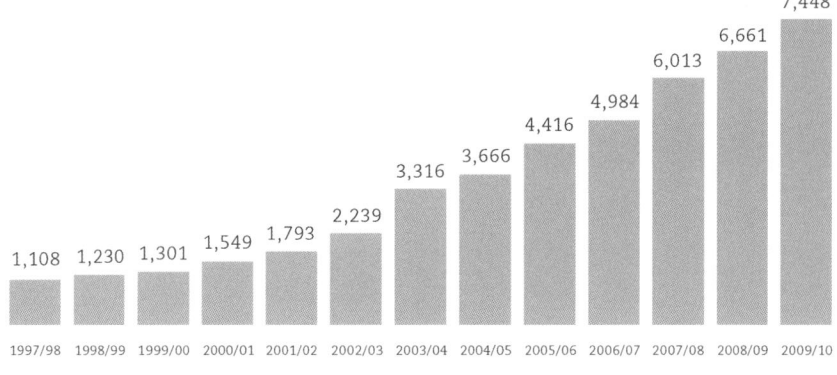

1997/98	1998/99	1999/00	2000/01	2001/02	2002/03	2003/04	2004/05	2005/06	2006/07	2007/08	2008/09	2009/10
1,108	1,230	1,301	1,549	1,793	2,239	3,316	3,666	4,416	4,984	6,013	6,661	7,448

Source: Department of Health

Social enterprises and the 'right to provide'

Social enterprises are organisations run on business lines, but which reinvest profits in the community or in service developments. They take different forms, and may include cooperatives, trusts or community interest companies. They number 62,000, contribute £24 billion to the economy and employ 800,000 people. A Social Enterprise Coalition survey in 2009 estimated that more than 6,000 social enterprises deliver health and social care within the NHS. They involve patients and staff in designing and delivering services, improving quality and tailoring services to meet patients' needs.

In 2008 the Labour Government introduced a 'right to request', under which primary care trust boards were obliged to consider requests from staff to leave the NHS and set up a social enterprise to provide services previously provided in-house. The first wave of 20 projects included schemes for homeless people, children and young people and mental health services. By the end of 2011, 57 social enterprises involving 25,000 staff had been 'spun out' from the NHS, delivering £900 million of services.

Building on the 'right to request', the coalition Government has launched its own 'right to provide' scheme and extended it to all health and social care staff. It believes staff-led enterprises reduce absenteeism and increase productivity, while giving professionals greater freedom to personalise and improve services.

Further information
Making quality your business: a guide to the right to provide, DH, March 2011.
Establishing social enterprises under the right to request programme, NAO, June 2011.
Office for Civil Society **www.civilsociety.co.uk**
Social Enterprise Coalition **www.socialenterprise.org.uk**

Managing the transition

As the Government announced its NHS reorganisation plans in July 2010 and most of the new structure will not be functioning fully until April 2013, the existing system has been adapted to manage the transition while attempting to reduce costs and achieve savings. For the NHS organisations that provide care, change will be minimal.

The ten SHAs – which acted as the local headquarters of the NHS, overseeing PCTs and NHS trusts – were organised into four clusters in October 2011. These are:
• London
• North (comprising North West, North East, and Yorkshire and Humber)
• Midlands (West Midlands, East Midlands and East of England)
• South (South West, South Central and South East Coast).

They will exist until April 2013 when their functions will pass to the NHS Commissioning Board – which will have sector offices covering the same geographical areas – and to other bodies in the new structure.

The 151 PCTs, which were responsible for commissioning and controlled 80 per cent of the NHS budget, have been reorganised into 50 clusters until their functions are transferred to clinical commissioning groups, the NHS Commissioning Board and local authorities by April 2013. The clusters represent collections of PCTs under a single executive team, which must ensure all PCTs continue to meet their legal, financial and performance obligations. Clusters also have a crucial role in helping develop the new commissioning system, especially nurturing CCGs, preparing for the NHS Commissioning Board, transferring public health to local government and setting up health and wellbeing boards. SHAs hold PCT clusters to account for delivering their responsibilities.

Further information
The legacy of primary care trusts, NHS Confederation/PCT Network, July 2011.
Public health transition planning support for primary care trusts and local authorities, DH/Local Government Association, January 2012.

Timetable

During 2012	Health Education England (see page 176) and the NHS Trust Development Authority established in shadow form
By October 2012	NHS Commissioning Board established as independent statutory body, initially with limited functions authorising CCGs
October 2012	Monitor begins to take on its new statutory functions (see page 148) HealthWatch England and local HealthWatch established (see page 139)
April 2013	SHAs and PCTs abolished and NHS Commissioning Board functioning fully Health Education England takes over SHAs' responsibilities for education and training NHS Trust Development Authority takes over SHAs' responsibilities for NHS trusts applying for foundation trust status Public Health England (see page 46) established A full system of CCGs established Health and wellbeing boards fully established
By April 2014	Remaining NHS trusts achieve foundation trust status
April 2016	Monitor's transitional powers of oversight over foundation trusts reviewed.

Key organisation: PCT Network

The NHS Confederation's PCT Network (PCTN) was established in 2007 to represent and support primary care trusts in England. The network has 98 per cent of PCT clusters in membership. In 2012/13, the network will continue to support these members during transition as PCT staff, functions and responsibilities are transferred to new organisations.

The NHS Confederation is also opening its membership to the emerging clinical commissioning groups which will become the local NHS commissioners from April 2013, and will help ensure all existing and new commissioners are working together to create strong, effective commissioning arrangements for the future.

www.nhsconfed.org/pctn

02 Commissioning

Commissioning is the process by which the NHS decides what services are needed, acquires them and then ensures they are being provided appropriately. It involves assessing the population's needs and deciding which are priorities, procuring the services to meet them and managing the providers. If done effectively, it ultimately ensures people live healthier and longer lives.

The origins of commissioning can be traced to the advent of the internal market in 1991 and the division of the NHS into purchasers and providers. Then it was referred to as 'purchasing'. The previous Labour Government introduced 'world-class commissioning', in an attempt to redress the general under-investment in skills development for commissioning that – along with frequent reorganisations – had hampered the discipline and left an imbalance in the influence that providers and commissioners exert over the system.

The coalition Government argued that 'commissioning has been too remote from the patients it is intended to serve', and decided responsibility for it should rest with healthcare professionals rather than managerial organisations. Healthcare professionals especially play a critical role in influencing NHS expenditure – for example, through referral and prescribing decisions. Clinical commissioning therefore gives them financial accountability for the consequences of their decisions. Clinical commissioning groups (CCGs) (see page 20), the NHS Commissioning Board (see page 18) and health and wellbeing boards (see page 22) are now replacing primary care trusts as the main commissioners of healthcare.

Further information
Liberating the NHS: commissioning for patients, DH, July 2010.
Commissioning: third report of session 2010–11, House of Commons health committee, January 2011.
Commissioning further issues: fifth report of session 2010–11, House of Commons health committee, March 2011.

The basics
The commissioning process comprises three broad activities – strategic planning, procurement and management – and is based on an eight-step cycle:
Assessing needs – systematically understanding the local population's health and care needs
Describing services and gap analysis – reviewing current services and defining the gaps (or over-provision) based on needs

Deciding priorities – using evidence of cost-effectiveness and based on a defensible ethical framework, deciding what to commission with available funds

Risk management – understanding key health and healthcare risks and deciding on a strategy to manage them

Strategic options – combining information into a single strategic commissioning plan that outlines how objectives will be met

Contract implementation – implementing the strategic plan through contracting

Provider development – including care pathway redesign and demand management, helping providers to improve – or decommission – services or introducing new providers

Managing provider performance – monitoring against contracts, using key performance indicators.

In addition, sound commissioning attempts to shift towards services that are personal, sensitive to individual need, and that maintain independence and dignity. It must focus on services and interventions that will achieve better health, promote inclusion and tackle health inequalities. It must also try to reorient towards promoting health and wellbeing, investing to reduce the future costs of ill health. It has therefore outgrown its fairly narrow traditional base of needs assessment and contracting.

Clinical commissioning groups' role

It is through CCGs that GPs and other healthcare professionals – including nurses, allied health professionals and pharmacists – will be responsible for commissioning most services to meet their patients' needs. CCGs will commission:

- community health services
- maternity services
- elective hospital care
- urgent and emergency care including ambulance and out-of-hours services
- older people's healthcare
- children's healthcare
- rehabilitation
- mental healthcare
- healthcare services for people with learning disabilities
- continuing healthcare.

A CCG may work in partnership with other CCGs or the NHS Commissioning Board to commission certain services across a wider area or take part in major service reconfiguration. CCGs may also agree to commission some health improvement services jointly with local authorities. This could include, for example, obesity, smoking cessation and drug and alcohol services. They will have a duty to promote integrated health and social care. CCGs cannot delegate commissioning decisions to private companies or contractors. This will not prevent them from using external agencies for commissioning support (see opposite) such as data analysis.

The NHS outcomes framework (see page 126) specifies the outcomes for which CCGs will be accountable. In planning services, CCGs will be involved in:
- identifying inequalities in access, quality and outcomes
- identifying indicators in the commissioning outcomes framework (see page 38) with scope for local improvement
- redesigning services or pathways to improve outcomes and better meet patients' needs
- identifying the most effective and cost-effective services, and planning new investments and disinvestments.

Every CCG must publish a commissioning plan before the start of each financial year, explaining how it intends to improve quality and outcomes, as well as fulfil its financial duties. In compiling this, the CCG must gather views from patients, carers, local communities, interest groups, health and wellbeing boards and local authorities. CCGs need to be able to translate individual patients' views into commissioning decisions, as well as act on the voice of each practice population. Their constituent practices should be significantly engaged, and they must also involve all other clinical colleagues – clinicians in secondary care, community and mental health, and learning disabilities, as well as public health experts and social care colleagues.

Once the plan is agreed, CCGs will place contracts with providers for the services they wish to commission. They must monitor providers' performance against these contracts, particularly in relation to quality and outcomes, patient experience, clinical standards, activity levels and spending.

Although health professionals will have overall responsibility for commissioning through their CCG, they are not expected to be involved in every commissioning function. Each CCG will have a management allowance to enable it to buy in – or share with other organisations – specialist expertise to support the non-clinical aspects of commissioning. Commercial, local authority, civil society and other organisations offer commissioning support skills such as analysing population health needs, managing contracts with providers and monitoring expenditure and outcomes.

Further information
The functions of GP commissioning consortia: a working document, DH, March 2011. *Discussion paper 11: Patient and public engagement in the new commissioning system*, NHS Confederation, October 2011.

Commissioning support services (CSSs)
NHS commissioning support services are being set up by primary care trusts to help CCGs, and will be hosted by the NHS Commissioning Board from April 2013. The DH intends them to become stand-alone enterprises, selling support services to CCGs, by April 2016. They may form commercial partnerships with private sector consultancies in order to draw on additional expertise when required. About 24 CSSs have been established so far, and they are unlikely to number many more in total.

Contracting for services
The 2012/13 NHS standard contract covers all agreements between commissioners and providers of NHS-funded acute hospital, ambulance, community, mental health and learning disability services. Separate NHS standard contracts are available for care homes and high-security services.

The contract creates legally binding agreements between commissioners, local authorities, foundation trusts, social enterprises, independent and voluntary sector providers. Agreements between commissioners and NHS trusts are not legally binding, but use the same documents and are treated as if they were.

The standard NHS contract has three parts:
• mandatory elements – which cannot be altered or removed
• required elements – which must be there, although the details are for agreement by the contracting parties
• additional elements – for which there is no national or legal requirement but which can be added by local agreement, provided they do not undermine mandatory or required elements.

Commissioning outcomes framework

The commissioning outcomes framework will measure the health outcomes and quality of care – including patient experience – achieved by CCGs. It is being developed by the NHS Commissioning Board supported by NICE (see page 148), in consultation with professional and patient groups.

The framework will enable the Board to identify CCGs' contribution to achieving the priorities for health improvement in the NHS outcomes framework (see page 126), while being accountable to patients and local communities. CCGs can also use it to benchmark their performance and identify priorities for improvement.

After consultation on indicators to be included in the framework, a final set are due to be published in October 2012 for use in 2013/14.

Further information

Commissioning outcomes framework: engagement document, NHS Commissioning Board, November 2011.

The contract provides a framework for holding providers to account for delivering high-quality NHS-funded services. It reflects the policy requirements of the NHS operating framework (see page 110) as well as patient choice (see page 64) and payment by results (see page 162).

Further information

Guidance on the NHS standard contract 2012/13, DH, December 2011.

NHS Commissioning Board's role

The NHS Commissioning Board will directly commission about £20 billion of services. These include:

- GP services, including GP-led health centres
- primary dental services
- eye care services
- community pharmaceutical services
- prison healthcare
- military healthcare
- high-security psychiatric services
- specialised services.

Obvious conflicts of interest will prevent CCGs commissioning most primary care, but they are expected to help the Board improve the quality of these services, and the Board can ask CCGs to carry out some commissioning functions relating to primary care on its behalf. CCGs are also expected to influence how the Board commissions other services.

Specialised services are those with low patient numbers but which need a critical mass of patients to make treatment centres cost-effective. Currently the NHS commissions over 50 specialised services, benefiting about 10,000 patients, at an annual cost of £480 million. They are provided in relatively few specialist centres to catchment populations of more than 1 million people. As they are high-cost, low-volume treatments, the risk to an individual or group of CCGs of having to fund expensive, unpredictable activity would be prohibitive. The specialised services portfolio is to be kept under regular review.

In addition, the Board will provide national leadership for commissioning. For example, it will set commissioning guidelines on the basis of clinically approved quality standards developed with advice from NICE (see page 148), and design model NHS contracts for CCGs to adapt for use with providers.

Health and wellbeing boards' role

Health and wellbeing boards (HWBs) will assess local needs through joint strategic needs assessments, and make collaborative decisions on how best to meet those needs through a joint health and wellbeing strategy. They will also have a crucial role in promoting joint commissioning and integrated provision of health, public health and social care services.

The aim is to ensure coherent and coordinated local commissioning plans across the NHS, public health and social care – for example, in relation to mental health, older people's or children's care, with intelligence about needs systematically shaping commissioning decisions. Through the HWB, councillors, public health directors and clinicians will have critical roles to play in the process.

HWBs should also be involved throughout development of CCGs' commissioning plans, which are expected to align with the health and wellbeing strategy. Although HWBs will not have a veto, they will have a right to refer plans back to the CCG or to the NHS Commissioning Board if they think plans do not take proper account of the strategy.

Joint strategic needs assessment

Joint strategic needs assessments (JSNAs) analyse populations' health needs to inform and guide commissioning of health, wellbeing and social care services within local authority areas. The NHS and upper-tier local authorities have had a statutory duty to produce an annual JSNA since 2007. The JSNA now has a central role in bringing together organisations from across the NHS, local government and the voluntary sector to analyse health needs. It is an essential part of the commissioning cycle, guiding decisions made at every stage from strategic planning and service provision through to monitoring and evaluation. The Government believes the advent of HWBs provides an opportunity to take existing JSNAs further through collaborative leadership and development of joint health and wellbeing strategies.

Conducting a needs assessment involves a wide range of quantitative and qualitative data, including patient, user and community views, to produce a comprehensive picture of current and future health needs for adults and children. Specialist skills and resources are needed to capture, collate, analyse and interpret population-level data.

The product is intended to improve health and wellbeing outcomes, and help address persistent health inequalities. The JSNA should guide CCGs, the local authority and the NHS Commissioning Board in deciding where to invest or reduce spending. Challenges may include integrating complex organisations with different agendas to agree on shared priorities, and organising CCGs that span several local authority areas to engage with the process.

In the past, most JSNAs have focused on a 'deficit' approach based on indicators of mortality and illness. Relatively few have been balanced by an assessment of the assets, strengths and capacities of local communities, which is clearly more desirable.

Joint health and wellbeing strategy

To meet the needs outlined in its JSNA, each HWB must develop a joint health and wellbeing strategy, setting local priorities for joint action. This should enable the HWB to plan integrated local services, and can be used to influence wider determinants of health. It will also be an opportunity for HWBs' constituent organisations to explore together local issues they have not managed to tackle on their own.

Joint health and wellbeing strategies provide the framework within which more detailed and specific commissioning plans for the NHS, social care, public health and other services are developed. Strategies should be 'concise and high-level', setting out how they will address a community's needs, rather than large, technical documents duplicating other plans.

Joint commissioning

The NHS and local government – in effect, CCGs and HWBs – will commission some services jointly. This should help integrate provision for patients, social care users and carers, connecting social care, public health and NHS services with aspects of the wider local authority agenda that affect health and wellbeing, such as housing and education.

HWBs can be the vehicle for 'lead commissioning' for particular services – for example, social care for people with long-term conditions – with pooled budgets and joint commissioning arrangements where the relevant functions are delegated to them. Tackling health inequalities will be a major priority for HWBs.

According to the Audit Commission, health and social care are still not working together closely enough despite years of efforts to improve joint working. It claims integrated care is not being achieved across England, with substantial differences persisting in the types of care received by people aged 65 or older. NHS and social care partners should be clearer about the outcomes they are trying to achieve and how they would know they were making progress towards them, the Commission said. Without good integration, there is a risk of wasted effort and 'cost-shunting', where savings made by one organisation or sector create costs for others.

(In Northern Ireland, health and social care have been combined since 1973, while Scotland intends to create health and social care partnerships, which will be the joint responsibility of the NHS and local authority.)

Further information

Briefing 221: The joint strategic needs assessment, NHS Confederation, July 2011.
Joint strategic needs assessment and joint health and wellbeing strategies explained, DH, December 2011.
Joining up health and social care: improving value for money across the interface, Audit Commission, December 2011.

Commissioning and competition

The coalition Government – like its Labour predecessor – sees competition as a 'tool' for commissioners to improve services. It argues: 'Properly regulated competition, when used appropriately, has the potential to improve the efficiency, quality and responsiveness of public services, to the benefit of those who use them and the taxpayer'. Competition is also instrumental in enabling commissioners to promote patient choice in line with the NHS Constitution (see page 112).

Nevertheless, competition has raised fears that:
• if left unchecked, it could destabilise the NHS
• it amounts to privatisation of the NHS
• EU competition law could be applied to the NHS, and be used to impose tendering, impede integrated care and destabilise hospital services.

In response, the Government has pledged: 'Competition will be used for one purpose and one purpose alone: as a means of improving the quality and responsiveness of services. Competition is not, and will not be used as an end in itself, and this Government is not ideologically bound to competition for its own sake.'

The Government initially intended that Monitor (see page 148) should take on a duty to promote competition, but in response to public disquiet it will instead focus on 'taking action in the interests of patients to tackle anti-competitive behaviour'. Monitor is being given concurrent powers with the Office of Fair Trading, to ensure competition rules can be applied by a sector-specific regulator with expertise in healthcare. It will also ensure commissioners properly apply UK and EU procurement law (see page 44).

After consulting Monitor and HealthWatch England (see page 139), the NHS Commissioning Board will issue guidance on how choice and competition should be applied to particular services. This will include advice on how services should be bundled or integrated. For example, where it would be in patients' interests, a commissioner could procure an entire care pathway from a single provider, as long as the process was fair, open and transparent. It is for commissioners to determine the shape of services, according to patients' preferences and needs. HealthWatch England will have power to establish a citizens' panel or similar arrangement to look at how choice and competition are working.

New legislation forbids moves to increase or maintain the market share of any particular sector or provider. This prevents any deliberate policy of encouraging the growth of the private sector over state providers, or vice versa.

The Government intends that competition should be based on quality, not price. The NHS Commissioning Board and Monitor will have a legal duty to develop standardised pricing 'currencies' for the national tariff (see page 162). Other safeguards include:

- Monitor's duty in setting the national tariff to ensure efficient providers are paid fairly, taking into account clinical complexity
- the NHS Commissioning Board's duty to extend standardised pricing currencies to services not yet covered by national prices
- a fixed tariff (national or local) for each service offered under the 'any qualified provider' policy (see page 25)
- payment by results (see page 162) ensuring fair prices are set for the potentially most profitable procedures that might be 'cherry-picked' by private providers
- commissioners having to follow 'best value' principles when tendering for non-tariff services, rather than simply choosing the lowest price
- providers' ability to turn away patients on clinical grounds only if there are strong and legitimate reasons for doing so, with such grounds normally agreed in advance
- a standard condition included in the licence Monitor issues to providers, ensuring transparency in patient referral or eligibility criteria
- contracts requiring providers to accept referred patients unless there are genuine and overriding clinical concerns
- commissioners' obligation to make public any variations to national tariff prices.

In addition, the principles and rules for cooperation and competition introduced by the previous Labour Government have been kept. The body that applies them, the Co-operation and Competition Panel, is transferring to Monitor but will retain its distinct identity.

Further information
Principles and rules for co-operation and competition, DH, March 2010.

Spotlight on policy: EU procurement law

Public bodies are subject to public procurement law, which regulates how they buy goods and services. The rules are derived from European Union law and policy, which aim to ensure free movement of goods and services within the EU and to open public sector contracts to competition. Broadly, this is achieved through requirements to advertise and competitively tender certain contracts, rather than simply awarding them to a chosen provider. Procurement law applies wherever a purchase exceeds the minimum financial thresholds set out by the legislation. These thresholds are low: for example, £156,442 for a clinical services contract.

As statutory public bodies, CCGs will be subject to the procurement rules and will need to comply with them when commissioning. The rules draw a distinction between Part A and Part B services. Health and social services fall within the lighter regime of Part B. This means that not all the detailed procurement rules imposed on Part A services apply. In particular, there is no legal requirement to comply with minimum timescales, or to follow one of the strict procedures set out by the procurement rules. There is also no requirement to advertise the contract in the *Official Journal of the European Union*.

However, some important principles of public procurement do apply. These include requirements to act transparently and treat providers equally and in a non-discriminatory way. For example, where there is potential for interest in a contract from a provider in another EU member state, the principle of transparency requires a contract to be subject to some form of advertising, proportionate to its scale and potential level of interest.

In buying non-clinical services – for example, management support – the full Part A procurement rules may apply, and full tendering processes may be necessary.

At the end of 2011 the EU proposed new procurement rules, which are currently subject to consultation. These would replace the distinction between Part A and B services but impose a higher threshold for health and social services contracts of 500,000 euros (about £418,000), above which EU procurement law would apply. Member states would be free to decide themselves what procedural rules to apply, so long as they respected the basic principles of transparency and equal treatment. Contract notices and awards above the new threshold would need to be advertised in *OJEU*.

Further information
Briefing 215: An introduction to procurement and competition for GP commissioners,
NHS Confederation, February 2011.

Public health

Public health is concerned with improving the population's health, rather than treating the diseases of individual patients. Safeguarding and enhancing public health is therefore an important objective of commissioning. The official definition of public health, devised by former chief medical officer Sir Donald Acheson, is: 'the science and art of preventing disease, prolonging life, and promoting health through the organised efforts of society'. Safeguarding and enhancing public health is therefore an important objective of commissioning.

Public health comprises three 'domains':
- health improvement – including lifestyles and wider social influences on health
- health protection – including infectious diseases, environmental hazards and emergencies
- health services – including service planning, efficiency, audit and evaluation.

Many of the aims of public health can only be achieved through partnerships across government departments and between the Government, NHS, local authorities, the private and voluntary sectors. This is especially true for tackling inequalities in health. Other major challenges include obesity, smoking, sexually transmitted infections, alcohol and drug misuse and improving mental health.

As part of its NHS reorganisation, the Government published a public health white paper, *Healthy lives, healthy people: our strategy for public health in England*, and proclaimed: 'This is a new era for public health, with a higher priority and dedicated resources'. Its intention is to create a new public health system in England, 'to protect and improve the public's health, improving the health of the poorest, fastest'. Although the NHS will still have a key role, local government is to take the lead. Its public health responsibilities already include environmental health, air quality, planning, transport and housing. Now upper-tier and unitary local authorities are to have a legal duty to improve their population's health, with new powers and ringfenced budgets to help them do so. A new body, Public Health England, will take a national lead.

Public Health England

Public Health England (PHE) is intended to be a national voice for public health, combining a number of national organisations and integrating health improvement, health protection and population health services into a single organisation.

As an executive agency of the DH, it will:
- provide impartial and scientifically rigorous advice on public health issues to the Government, public and others
- provide advice, support, evidence and intelligence to local authorities and CCGs
- develop ways to enable individuals and communities to improve health and wellbeing
- provide microbiology and health protection services, and together with local authorities lead the public health response in emergencies
- work with the devolved administrations on UK-wide issues – for example, on chemical hazards and radiological protection.

It will have its own chief executive, who will have operational independence. It will also have a national office – including national centres and hubs that work with the NHS Commissioning Board – and units that support local authorities in their area.

PHE will provide leadership for the public health profession and professional support for directors of public health. It is intended to bring together the functions of a range of bodies that currently employ 4,500 and carry out diverse roles. They are:
- Health Protection Agency
- National Treatment Agency for substance misuse
- the nine public health observatories in England
- cancer registries and the National Cancer Intelligence Network
- national screening committee and cancer screening programmes.

Locally, PHE will generate information on the state of public health in England to support development of JSNAs and joint health and wellbeing strategies (see page 40). It will also work with academic researchers and public health practitioners to build an evidence base of effective interventions, ensuring they share best practice and achieve value for money. It will monitor local authorities' contributions to achieving the public health outcomes framework (see page 49).

PHE will play a particularly key role in protecting people from hazards, including infectious diseases, radiation, chemicals and poisons, and any emergencies they cause.

PHE is due to take on its full responsibilities in April 2013.

Further information
Public Health England's operating model – factsheets, DH, December 2011.

Local authorities and public health
The Government says local authorities are best placed to tackle the wider determinants of health such as employment, education, environment, housing and transport, and so are a natural home for a public health function. Their new responsibilities include:
- tobacco control
- alcohol and drug misuse services
- obesity and community nutrition initiatives
- increasing physical activity
- public mental health services
- dental public health services
- accidental injury prevention
- population-level interventions to reduce and prevent birth defects
- campaigns to prevent cancer and long-term conditions
- local initiatives on workplace health
- supporting, reviewing and challenging NHS services such as immunisation programmes
- comprehensive sexual health services
- promoting community safety, violence prevention and response
- local initiatives to tackle social exclusion.

In addition, they will be responsible for the National Child Measurement Programme, NHS Health Check assessment and elements of the Healthy Child Programme. Local authorities will be funded to carry out their new public health responsibilities through a ringfenced grant. Within local authorities, HWBs will be the focus of the public health system, promoting joint commissioning and driving improvements in the local population's health and wellbeing (see page 39). Local authorities will take on their new public health responsibilities in April 2013.

Further information
Public health in local government – factsheets, DH, December 2011.

Directors of public health

The director of public health (DPH) for each local authority will embed public health across the authority, 'acting corporately but exercising the appropriate professional independence where necessary to advocate for the health of the local population'. The DPH will be:
- the principal adviser on health to elected members and officials
- charged with delivering key new public health functions
- a statutory member of the HWB
- the author of an annual report on the health of the population.

The DPH will lead on investment for improving and protecting the local population's health, and on reducing health inequalities through the way the ringfenced grant is spent – although the authority's chief executive remains accountable for the grant.

On health protection, DPHs will work with PHE locally and with the NHS to ensure appropriate public health responses to potential problems, from local incidents and outbreaks to emergencies.

On population healthcare, DPHs and their teams will provide public health expertise, advice and analysis to CCGs and HWBs and – for primary care and other directly commissioned services – to the NHS Commissioning Board.

DPHs will be appointed jointly by their local authority and PHE.

NHS and public health

The NHS's role in securing population health outcomes includes:
- providing healthcare to meet the local population's needs
- providing population health interventions such as childhood immunisations and national screening programmes
- contributing to health protection and emergency response.

If the NHS uses its millions of contacts with patients every year to provide advice, brief interventions and referrals, it can make an impact on public health by supporting people to live healthier lives. The NHS will also continue to play an important role in commissioning and providing public health services.

Further information
The NHS's role in the public's health: a report form the NHS Future Forum, DH, January 2012.

Key text: Public health outcomes framework

The public health outcomes framework concentrates on two high-level outcomes to be achieved across the public health system:

- increased healthy life expectancy
- reduced differences in life expectancy and healthy life expectancy between communities.

As improvements will take years or decades before marked change is evident, 66 supporting indicators will measure national and local progress annually across four 'domains':

- improving the wider determinants of health
- health improvement
- health protection
- healthcare public health and preventing premature mortality.

Progress will be judged against results such as:

- fewer children under five with tooth decay
- people weighing less
- more women breastfeeding their babies
- fewer people over 65 suffering falls
- fewer people smoking
- fewer people dying from heart disease and stroke.

Further information

Improving outcomes and supporting transparency – part 1: a public health outcomes framework for England 2013–2016, DH, January 2012.

Secretary of State's role

The Secretary of State's responsibilities for public health include:

- setting a ringfenced budget for public health from within the overall health budget
- setting the direction for PHE and the context for local public health efforts
- leading public health across central government, through the Cabinet sub-committee on public health
- setting the national public health outcomes framework (see above)
- holding PHE to account
- leading public health work across civil society and with business, and brokering national partnerships

- participating in public health work across the UK with the devolved administrations and at European and international levels
- proposing legislation where necessary
- commissioning research for public health through the National Institute for Health Research (see page 189).

Further information

Healthy lives, healthy people: our strategy for public health in England, HM Government, November 2010.

Healthy lives, healthy people: update and way forward, HM Government, July 2011.

Public health: twelfth report of session 2010–12, House of Commons health committee, October 2011.

The new public health system: summary, DH, December 2011.

Improving the public's health

Improvements in public health have brought dramatic gains. People in England are healthier and live longer than ever before, while infectious diseases now account for only one in 50 deaths. Mortality rates for cancer and circulatory diseases are declining, and reducing faster in England than the EU average. The percentage of those who smoke is also falling. Infant deaths in England in 2009 were the lowest ever: fewer than five per 1,000 live births compared with 18 per 1,000 in 1970. However, infant deaths remain higher than some European countries.

Causes of premature death among adults are dominated by 'lifestyle diseases' – often underpinned by mental health – involving tobacco, alcohol, diet and lack of exercise. Smoking still kills 80,000 people every year, while levels of harm from alcohol are rising: mortality rates for chronic liver disease and cirrhosis in England have risen above the EU average. Britain is the most obese nation in Europe, and has a large population of problem drug users. Rates of sexually transmitted infections are high and rising, while teenage conceptions – at a 20-year low – remain high compared with Europe.

Perhaps most strikingly, even where improvements are apparent, health inequalities between rich and poor have been getting progressively worse, and the wealthy can expect to live seven years longer than the poor.

The Government says health and wellbeing are influenced by social, cultural, economic, psychological and environmental factors throughout life, and has identified opportunities for improving public health at birth, in childhood, adulthood, old age and at work. It argues that every sector of

• Children from manual social backgrounds are 1.5 times as likely to die during infancy than those from non-manual backgrounds
• The rate of infant deaths is 70 per cent higher in the West Midlands than in the South East
• UK infant mortality rates are higher than in France, Spain, Germany and Italy
• Manchester men have the lowest life expectancy in England – 73 years. Men in Kensington and Chelsea can expect to live until they are 83.1 years old. The national average is 77.4 years
• People from black and minority ethnic groups are up to six times more likely to develop diabetes
• People in lower socio-economic groups are 50 per cent more likely to smoke
• Obesity levels are nearly 50 per cent higher among women from lower socio-economic groups.

Source: Department of Health

society can contribute to public health. Acknowledging that charities, voluntary organisations and community groups already make a vital contribution, it wants businesses to take more responsibility for their impact on health and wellbeing, and argues that employers should support their staff's health. Central government will play an important role in health protection and enabling local communities to reduce health inequalities, while individuals should feel they are in control of all aspects of their health, wellbeing and care.

Further information
DH Campaigns Resource Centre http://campaigns.dh.gov.uk

Tackling health inequalities
Health inequalities start early in life, persist into old age and are repeated in subsequent generations. They exist in many forms. Different regions have different health outcomes. Children born in lower socio-economic backgrounds are more likely to die at birth, suffer more illness throughout their life and die younger. Unemployment and poor housing, in particular, are significant causes of ill health. Ethnicity also plays a major role, with a higher prevalence of disease among different racial groups. Health inequality is found by gender, disability, sexual orientation and lifestyle. It is both avoidable and fundamentally unfair.

NHSCONFEDERATION

Tackling health inequalities and improving health require active commitment by government departments and groups at all levels – national, regional and local. Joint working, partnerships, networking, shared funding and resources are crucial.

Under the previous Government the DH commissioned a strategic review of health inequalities by Professor Sir Michael Marmot, focusing on how the social determinants of health influence health inequalities. It identified six policy objectives that require action if health inequalities are to be reduced:

- give every child the best start in life
- enable all children, young people and adults to maximise their capabilities and have control over their lives
- create fair employment and good work for all
- ensure a healthy standard of living for all
- create and develop healthy and sustainable places and communities
- strengthen the role and impact of ill health prevention.

Marmot said that achieving these objectives would need action by central and local government, the NHS, the third and private sectors and community groups. National policies would not work without effective local delivery systems focused on health equity in all policies. Effective local delivery required 'effective participatory decision-making at local level', which could only happen by empowering individuals and local communities.

The University College London Institute of Health Equity, led by Sir Michael Marmot, will receive £1 million funding over the next three years from the DH. It will collect evidence, provide advice and share local and international best practice on reducing health inequalities.

Further information

UCL Institute of Health Equity **www.instituteofhealthequity.org**
Fair society, healthy lives: the Marmot review, Marmot Review, February 2010.
Health profile of England 2009, DH, March 2010.
Our health and wellbeing today, HM Government, November 2010.
Tackling inequalities in life expectancy in areas with the worst health and deprivation: third report of session 2010–11, House of Commons public accounts committee, October 2011.

Health Work Wellbeing

Health Work Wellbeing is a government-led initiative to improve the health and wellbeing of working-age people. Founded on evidence that working is good for health, it brings together employers, unions and healthcare professionals to help more people with health conditions find and stay in employment. A cross-government programme, it was launched in 2005 by the DH, Department for Work and Pensions and the Health and Safety Executive. It now also includes the Scottish and Welsh Governments.

Its aim is 'to break the link between ill health and inactivity, to advance the prevention of ill health and injury, to encourage good management of occupational health, and to transform opportunities for people to recover from illness while at work'.

The strategy is led by a national director for health and work, Dame Carol Black, who found that ill health cost £100 billion a year and that access to good work-related health support was inadequate in the early stages of sickness, with provision disproportionately concentrated among a few large employers, leaving most without support. She proposed:

- piloting a Fit for Work service for patients in the early stages of illness
- if successful, the service to be extended to those on incapacity and other out-of-work benefits
- the traditional 'sick note' to be replaced by an electronic 'fit note' stating what people can do rather than what they cannot
- occupational health to be brought into the mainstream of healthcare provision.

The then Labour Government accepted most of the recommendations and those in a report into NHS staff health and wellbeing, led by Dr Steve Boorman (see page 185). The coalition Government has since endorsed both.

Further information

Health, work and wellbeing – caring for our future: a strategy for the health and wellbeing of working age people, DWP, DH & HSE, October 2005.

Working for a healthier tomorrow, TSO, March 2008.

Improving health and work: changing lives – the Government's response to Dame Carol Black's review of the health of Britain's working-age population, TSO, November 2008.

Health, work and well-being indicators: progress update report, DH, DWP and partners, December 2011.

coping with a flu pandemic

Every year seasonal flu affects thousands of people across the UK, mainly in winter. But occasionally, with unpredictable frequency, a different strain of flu virus emerges and spreads rapidly across the world, causing a pandemic. Large swathes of the population can become infected relatively quickly. The virus may be associated with mild to moderate illness or significant severe illness and mortality in certain age or patient groups, and it could disrupt the normal functioning of society. A new flu pandemic is therefore recognised as a serious threat facing the UK, and plans over and above those for seasonal flu are needed.

Since the last flu pandemic – the 2009 H1N1 outbreak, which was mild compared to previous pandemics – the UK has updated its strategy. For the first time, the plan sets out the main phases of a pandemic and the likely scenarios of low, moderate or high impact. Each scenario comprises four sections:
- nature and scale of the illness – what defines the need for the pandemic to have reached this level
- key healthcare delivery – specific actions and guidance for healthcare providers
- impact on society – how the pandemic may affect local communities
- public messages – reassurance and specific information for the general public.

The plan builds on guidance and experience from 2009, particularly the need for a response proportionate to the severity of the virus's impact rather than just focusing on the 'worst case' planning assumptions. The strategy has been developed jointly across the four UK Governments, and the World Health Organization says the UK remains among the leaders worldwide in preparing for a pandemic.

Further information

The 2009 influenza pandemic: an independent review of the UK response to the 2009 influenza pandemic, Cabinet Office, January 2010.
UK influenza pandemic preparedness strategy 2011, DH and devolved administrations, November 2011.

Responsibility Deal

The Public Health Responsibility Deal has been established to tap into the potential for businesses and other organisations to improve public health and tackle health inequalities through their influence over food, alcohol, physical activity and health in the workplace. The initiative aims to bring together industry, consumer organisations, health professionals and others to voluntarily agree action they can take to help people lead healthier lives. It emphasises partnership rather than 'top-down government intervention'.

The deal's participants sign up to 'core commitments' and 'supporting pledges' for action, covering food, physical activity, alcohol and health in the workplace. By the end of 2011, more than 300 organisations had signed the deal.

Certain issues have been ruled out, including tax, pricing and matters that may breach competition law. Some public health professionals have responded sceptically to the initiative, but the Government denies the deal has handed power over public health policy to business: 'The Public Health Responsibility Deal is not a substitute for the development of government policy, but complements it'. It argues that commercial organisations have influence with and can reach consumers in ways that Government cannot.

The deal's main decision-making body is a plenary group chaired by the Secretary of State, and includes representatives from industry, the retail sector, voluntary sector, non-governmental organisations and local government.

Further information

The Public Health Responsibility Deal, DH, March 2011.
http://responsibilitydeal.dh.gov.uk

Public health workforce

Public health professionals monitor the health status of the community, identify health needs, develop programmes to reduce risk and screen for early disease, control communicable disease, promote health, plan and evaluate healthcare provision and manage and implement change.

The public health workforce comprises people in a range of disciplines who work in one of three categories:
• health improvement and reducing inequalities: teachers, local business leaders, managers, social workers, transport engineers, housing officers, other local government staff and the voluntary sector, as well as doctors,

Spotlight on policy: tackling climate change

The potential impacts of climate change on health are many and varied. In the UK, hotter drier summers, milder wetter winters, more flooding and heat waves could mean:

• fewer cold-related winter deaths and more heat-related summer deaths
• more cases of food poisoning and insect-borne diseases
• more cases of sunburn and skin cancer.

In 2007 the NHS was responsible for 21 million tonnes of carbon dioxide a year – more than 3 per cent of England's emissions – and for 25 per cent of public sector emissions. Its carbon reduction strategy commits the NHS to a 10 per cent reduction in its 2007 carbon footprint by 2015. By 2050 the NHS must reduce the footprint by 80 per cent of its 1990 level. NHS organisations must now include sustainability data in their annual reports.

A web portal to help healthcare organisations cut carbon emissions and energy use has been created by University College London Hospitals and the Building Research Establishment.

The NHS Sustainable Development Unit (SDU) was set up in 2008. Its small team based in Cambridge aims to:

• provide leadership, expertise and guidance on sustainable development
• promote a culture of measurement and management that underpins carbon governance
• help shape NHS policy locally, nationally and internationally
• evaluate and cost best practice and innovations on sustainability, helping the NHS with implementation.

SDU has published a 'route map' to help organisations progress towards a sustainable healthcare system.

The NHS Forest project intends to plant 1.3 million trees – one for every NHS employee – as part of a plan to create wooded areas equivalent to 2,500 football pitches on NHS sites. UK-wide, it is coordinated by the Centre for Sustainable Healthcare, which says that when the forest reaches maturity in 20 years' time it will reduce the NHS's carbon footprint by 10 per cent. By the beginning of 2012, it had planted 7,148 trees.

Further information

Saving carbon, improving health: NHS carbon reduction strategy update, NHS SDU, January 2010.
Route map for sustainable health, NHS SDU, February 2011.
NHS Sustainable Development Unit **www.sdu.nhs.uk**
Sustainability portal **www.bre.co.uk/sdhealth**
NHS Forest **http://nhsforest.org**

nurses and other healthcare professionals
• public health practice: health visitors, environmental health officers and community development workers, and those who use research, information, public health science or health promotion skills in specific public health fields
• public health consultants and specialists, who work at a strategic or senior management level or at a senior level of scientific expertise.

For about the last ten years, non-medically qualified specialists have been able to hold high-level public health posts, such as DPH. Formerly, public health professionals were almost all doctors. Public health consultants with a medical or dental background are regulated under the statutory regulatory frameworks of the General Medical Council (see page 153) and the General Dental Council (see page 154).

Others are regulated under the voluntary and independent UK Public Health Register. This is designed to inform the public and employers that multi-disciplinary specialists in public health are qualified, competent and meet expected standards. The Government is consulting on whether regulation of all public health consultants and specialists should be mandatory, with the Health Professions Council being made responsible for this.

The Faculty of Public Health is responsible for standard-setting within the public health profession in the UK.

Further information

Review of the regulation of public health professionals, DH, November 2010.
Faculty of Public Health **www.fph.org.uk**

tobacco control

More than 80,000 people die in England each year from smoking-related diseases – more than all deaths from alcohol, road traffic and other accidents, suicide, illegal drugs and diabetes combined. Smoking causes 18 per cent of all deaths in those aged over 35, while 6 per cent of children aged 11–15 are regular smokers. Smoking is estimated to cost the NHS in England £2.7 billion a year, and the overall cost to society is estimated at £14 billion a year.

Since the early 1970s, adult smoking rates have been cut from 45 per cent to 21 per cent in 2008. Seven out of ten current smokers want to give up smoking, and six in ten try to quit each year. Smoking in enclosed public places was banned in Scotland in March 2006 followed by Wales and Northern Ireland in April 2007 and England in July 2007. Selling tobacco from vending machines was banned in England in October 2011 and in Wales and Northern Ireland in March 2012; a ban in Scotland has been delayed by a legal challenge. The display of tobacco products has been banned in large shops since April 2012, and the ban will extend to all other shops from 2015. The Government is to hold a public consultation on plain packaging of tobacco products.

The Government's tobacco control plan aims to reduce smoking rates in England by the end of 2015:
- from 21.2 to 18.5 per cent or less among adults
- from 15 to 12 per cent or less among 15-year-olds
- from 14 to 11 per cent or less among pregnant mothers.

These targets exceed the reductions in smoking that have occurred in the last five years. Action will focus on:
- stopping promotion of tobacco
- making tobacco less affordable
- effective regulation of tobacco products
- helping tobacco users to quit
- reducing exposure to secondhand smoke
- effective communications for tobacco control.

Further information

Healthy lives, healthy people: a tobacco control plan for England, DH, March 2011.

03 Providing services

NHS organisations provide a wide range of services, outside hospitals and within them. Historically, hospitals have dominated the NHS's resources, but today much more care can be provided in GP surgeries and health centres closer to people's homes – and it is government policy that it should be. It wants patients to have much more choice than hitherto over where they are treated, and it wants the services provided to feel more personal, taking greater account of people's preferences than was customary in the past.

Primary care

Primary care is normally the patient's first point of consultation with the health service. It is concerned with promoting health as well as treating and managing conditions that do not require specialist care in hospital. For NHS patients, primary care provides the key to navigating the rest of the healthcare system: GPs, community nurses, health visitors, allied health professionals, pharmacists, dentists and opticians have a role as advocates for patients needing services from other parts of the NHS. Providing continuity of care is another important aspect.

About 90 per cent of NHS patients receive their treatment in primary care, and over 300 million consultations take place every year in England alone. Advances, especially in diagnostics and minor surgery, mean many more treatments once carried out in hospital can be performed in primary care – a rapidly growing trend convenient for patients and of benefit to the system as a whole. Over 5 million people in England live more than ten miles from their nearest hospital.

A wide range of staff work in primary care in England. In 2010 there were:
• 39,409 GPs
• 21,325 practice nurses
• 98,330 practice staff, including practice managers, receptionists, IT support and notes summarisers, physiotherapists, podiatrists, counsellors, phlebotomists and healthcare assistants.

The NHS was ranked as having one of the world's best primary care systems in a 2009 survey of 10,000 physicians in 11 developed countries by the Commonwealth Fund, a US think tank. It was rated top in several categories.

Further information
The Commonwealth Fund international health policy survey 2009, Commonwealth Fund, November 2009.
www.commonwealthfund.org

General practitioners

Most GP practices are independent contractors and are run as partnerships, while specialist companies run some practices. The number of practices has fallen from 9,090 in 1998 to 8,324 in 2010, although the number of GPs has increased, suggesting practices have become bigger: the average number of patients per practice has risen from 5,624 to 6,610 in that time. The average number of patients per GP was 1,567. Single-handed GPs have fallen in number by 28 per cent to 1,408 in the five years to 2009.

GPs held on average 87 surgery and 17 telephone consultations a week and made five home visits in 2006/07, according to the last GP workload survey. Each surgery consultation lasted 12 minutes on average, and each phone consultation seven minutes.

Under the general medical services contract, all GP practices are required to provide 'essential services': they must manage patients who are ill or believe themselves to be ill, giving health promotion advice and making referrals as necessary. They must also manage patients who are terminally ill and those with chronic diseases. All practices are expected to provide 'additional services' such as contraception or childhood immunisations, but they can opt out of them. They may also choose to provide 'enhanced services' in response to need, such as minor surgery, specialised services for patients with multiple sclerosis and specialised sexual health services. The quality and outcomes framework (see page 122) is designed to maintain high standards and broaden the range of services GPs offer.

The Government is keen for GPs to widen their role to include services traditionally found only in hospitals. It believes that those with accredited specialist skills could handle more minor operations, while specially trained GPs and senior consultants should routinely work together in community hospitals and health centres. Operations for conditions such as cataracts, hernias and varicose veins can be done on the same site, reducing waiting times and potentially saving money.

Pilot projects are underway in London, Manchester and Nottingham to offer people greater choice of GP practice. Patients will no longer be restricted to registering with a practice near their home, but can choose one close to work, to a relative they care for or to a child's school. The pilots are also testing arrangements to enable people away from home to use a GP surgery as a non-registered patient.

The 2010/11 GP patient survey found:
• 94 per cent of patients have confidence and trust in their doctor
• 90 per cent of patients are satisfied with the care they receive at their surgery
• 89 per cent of patients say their doctor gives them enough time
• 83 per cent of patients would recommend their GP surgery to someone new to their area.

Further information
Choice of GP practice – guidance for PCTs, DH, January 2012.
GP patient survey results **www.gp-patient.co.uk**

Practitioners with a special interest
One way in which primary care services are expanding is by developing the role of practitioners with special interests.

GPs with a special interest (GPSIs) have additional training and expertise enabling them to provide a clinical service beyond the scope of normal general practice, undertake advanced procedures or develop services. They take referrals from colleagues for conditions in specialties such as ophthalmology, orthopaedics, dermatology and ear, nose and throat surgery, or undertake diagnostic procedures such as endoscopy. GPSIs do not offer a full consultant service, replace consultants or interfere with access to consultants by local GPs. Typically they undertake two sessions a week in their specialty.

GPSIs can increase the capacity of primary care to undertake outpatient appointments, reduce patient waiting times, provide a more convenient service and help to free consultant time in secondary care. Over 1,750 GPSIs are currently practising.

GP out-of-hours services

'Out-of-hours' usually refers to the period from 6:30pm Monday to Thursday until 8am the following day, and from 6:30pm on Friday until 8am on the following Monday, as well as public holidays.

About 75 per cent of out-of-hours provision is carried out by GP cooperatives and 25 per cent by commercial providers, ambulance trusts and others, with NHS Direct supplying initial call-handling for many providers.

A DH review, following the death of a patient after treatment by a locum GP from Germany, found unacceptable variation in how out-of-hours services are commissioned and monitored. Its 24 recommendations included:
- guidance to assist commissioners in making decisions about whether a doctor has the necessary knowledge of English
- out-of-hours providers to consider recruitment and selection processes for clinical staff
- providers to cooperate with each other to share concerns over staff working excessive hours for their services.

Further information
General practice out of hours services: project to consider and assess current arrangements, Dr David Colin Thomé and Professor Steve Field, DH, January 2010.

Initially, emphasis was on developing GPs with special interests, but dentists and pharmacists have now been included. Nurses and allied health professionals have developed their own approaches without adopting the terminology. A national accreditation framework for GPs and pharmacists with a special interest was launched in 2007 to ensure standards of care in the community are equivalent to those in acute care. PCTs have accreditation panels to verify GPs' and pharmacists' skills. Re-accreditation is carried out within three years.

Research has shown that while GPSI services improve access, they can be more costly than hospital clinics.

patient choice

Since 2008, all patients referred for an elective procedure have been given a 'free choice' of any hospital, clinic or treatment centre in England that met NHS standards and price, including those in the independent sector. This became a legal right under the NHS Constitution (see page 112) in 2009. The coalition Government, in its *Liberating the NHS* white paper, announced: 'In future, patients and carers will have far more clout and choice in the system'. Patients are now being given choice not only of provider, but of consultant-led team, GP practice and treatment.

DH research revealed more than 80 per cent of patients want more choice over how and where they are treated in the NHS, and nearly three-quarters want more choice in who provides their hospital care. Meanwhile, the NHS Co-operation and Competition Panel (see page 43) found that offering a choice of provider was helping the NHS achieve 'higher quality care, greater accessibility, and more efficient delivery in services'.

Under the 'any qualified provider' policy (see page 25), patients referred for selected services can choose from a range of providers who meet NHS quality, prices and contracts. Previously, choice was only available in non-urgent hospital care, but it has now been extended to community and mental health services. Eight services, including those for back pain, continence, wheelchairs and talking therapies, have been identified as the most suitable to offer patients choice. Every area will be expected to offer more choice in a minimum of three services by September 2012 – either from the recommended list or for another community or mental health service that is a high local priority. The number will be expanded further from April 2013.

Since April 2012, NHS providers have had to accept all clinically appropriate referrals to named hospital consultant-led teams for a first outpatient appointment for elective care. No geographical boundaries are imposed on referrals, and NHS providers will have to publish relevant information about their consultants and the services they provide. Services currently excluded from this are A&E, cancer services subject to the two-week maximum waiting time, maternity, mental health and any other services involving urgent care.

The Government has banned commissioners from enforcing minimum waiting times on referrals and imposing caps on the number of patients a provider will be paid for treating. Some primary care trusts were doing this to manage demand and help balance their budgets.

To help choose a provider, patients can use a national directory of services that is part of the Choose and Book facility on the NHS Choices website (see page 205), which also lets them choose a time and date for their appointment. Information includes location, waiting times, reputation, clinical performance, visiting policies, parking facilities and other patients' comments.

Choose and Book is currently used for about 50 per cent of NHS referral activity from GP surgery to first outpatient appointment – more than 500,000 appointments a month plus another 150,000 a month for services offered by allied health professionals (see page 69). More than 25 million appointments have been booked using Choose and Book and more than 95 per cent of all GP practices have used it to refer patients.

Further information
Liberating the NHS: greater choice and control – a consultation on proposals, DH, October 2010.
Review of the operation of 'any willing provider' for the provision of routine elective care: final report, NHS Co-operation and Competition Panel, July 2011.
NHS Choices **www.nhs.uk**
Choose and Book **www.chooseandbook.nhs.uk**

Redesigning the fabric of primary care

The GP surgery is the focus of most primary care and the source of ever wider-ranging services. Over the past decade the NHS has invested in modern multi-purpose premises where GPs work alongside nurses, pharmacists, dentists, therapists, opticians, midwives and social care staff. Commissioners were encouraged to set up one-stop health centres – sometimes referred to as 'supersurgeries' or polyclinics – which bring services such as GPs, health visitors, dentists, a pharmacy, a cardiology clinic, x-ray facilities and optometry under one roof. About 750 such centres have been built since 2001, and 3,000 other GP premises – about a third of the total – substantially refurbished or replaced.

The previous Labour Government requested all 150 primary care trusts to set up a GP-led health centre to be open 12 hours a day seven days a week, offering walk-in services and holding their own lists of registered patients. London was to take them a step further with polyclinics offering diagnostic and other services traditionally provided in hospitals. By 2010, all but a handful of PCTs had opened GP-led health centres and London had seven polyclinics. However, some GP-led health centres have since closed, where demand for their services proved less than expected. The coalition Government has halted London's polyclinic programme, which it saw as a 'top-down, one-size-fits-all approach'.

About 90 NHS walk-in centres throughout England provide fast access to advice and treatment for minor ailments and injuries without an appointment. They see 3 million patients a year. Walk-in centres – also known as minor injury units or urgent care centres – are open seven days a week, from 7am to 10pm, and offer assessment by an experienced NHS nurse as well as information on out-of-hours GP, dental and local pharmacy services. The centres are helping improve access for groups with particular needs, including young or homeless people. An established walk-in centre sees around 2,500 patients per month.

Dental services
Most dentists in primary care are self-employed and contract their services to the NHS, like most GPs. They numbered 22,799 in 2010/11.

Access to dentistry has been a high-profile issue for almost 20 years, with concerns about gaps in access to NHS-funded services and practices opting out or closing to new NHS patients. Policy on dental services lagged behind other health sectors until 2006, when over 400 charges for treatment were replaced by three standard charges for all treatments under a revised dental contract. The £2.8 billion budget for primary care dental services was devolved to commissioners, and covered surgery salaries and expenses instead of the piecework pay system set up when the NHS was founded. However, the 2006 contract did not succeed in encouraging preventive care rather than focusing on a fee-per-item approach, and dentists widely perceived it as unfair.

A new dental contract is now being piloted in 70 practices, structured to reward dentists for continuity and quality of care rather than the number of treatments undertaken. It is based on registration, capitation and quality. Its aim is to improve care quality, increase access to dental services and improve oral health, especially children's.

Further information
NHS dental contract: proposals for pilots, DH, December 2010.

Community pharmacies
Britain's 10,951 high street pharmacies dispensed 80.7 million prescription items in 2010/11. They increasingly offer services traditionally available only at GPs' surgeries. The pharmacy contract introduced in 2005 aims to improve the range and quality of services of the community pharmacy and integrate it more into the NHS. It defines three tiers of service:
• Essential services must be provided by all community pharmacists. They include dispensing, disposal of medication and support for self-care.
• Advanced services require the pharmacist to have accreditation and/or their premises to meet certain standards. So far, medicines use review and prescription intervention fall in this category.
• Enhanced services are commissioned locally. Examples include minor ailment schemes and smoking-cessation services.

Many pharmacies now offer new services such as:
• repeat prescribing, so that patients can get up to a year's supply of medicines without having to revisit their GP
• clinics for people with conditions such as diabetes, high blood pressure or high cholesterol
• signposting other health and social care services and supporting self-care
• consultation areas.

Further information
The new contractual framework for community pharmacy, DH, October 2004.

Opticians
There were 10,409 ophthalmic practitioners in England in 2010/11, and 11.9 million NHS eye tests were carried out. There are three kinds of registered optician:

Optometrists – or ophthalmic opticians – carry out eye tests, look for signs of eye disease and prescribe and fit glasses and contact lenses. They are graduates who have undertaken a three- or four-year degree in optometry, then spent at least a year in supervised practice before taking professional exams leading to registration with the General Optical Council. There were 10,079 registered optometrists in England in 2010.

Dispensing opticians fit and sell glasses, and interpret prescriptions, but do not test eyes. Some dispense low-vision aids, and some are qualified to fit contact lenses under instruction from an optometrist.

Ophthalmic medical practitioners are doctors specialising in eyes and eye care. There were 330 in England in 2010. They work to the same terms of service as optometrists.

In addition, ophthalmologists are doctors specialising in eye diseases and most perform eye surgery. They usually work in hospital eye departments. Orthoptists treat disorders of binocular vision, and work in eye departments under the supervision of ophthalmologists. They may also undertake visual screening of children in the community. Some GPs have a special interest in ophthalmology, while ophthalmic nurses and ophthalmic technicians – or ophthalmic science practitioners – also provide services.

Optometrists are independent contractors. Some have specialist skills – for example, in contact lenses, low vision or paediatrics – and can treat patients who would otherwise have to be seen in hospital. Most practices have much of the equipment found in ophthalmology clinics.

Under co-management, or shared care, optometrists working to an agreed protocol undertake specified clinical procedures designed to relieve GPs and the hospital eye service, as well as move patient care into the community. This may cover conditions such as glaucoma, diabetes, cataracts and minor acute eye problems. Throughout the UK, optometrists can now prescribe medicines for conditions of the eye and surrounding tissue if they are registered to do so with the General Optical Council and have undertaken special training.

The 2007 general optical service review assessed how eye-care services are currently provided and found potential for eye-care professionals in primary care to work alongside hospitals in developing more responsive services for patients with eye conditions such as glaucoma. It also identified scope for greater collaboration between the NHS, social care and the third sector in providing integrated services for patients with low-vision problems and in taking wider action to improve eye health.

General ophthalmic services review: findings in relation to the framework for primary ophthalmic services, the position of dispensing opticians in relation to the NHS, local optical committees, and the administration of General Ophthalmic Services payments, DH, January 2007.

Community health services

Community health services are a major part of the NHS, employing 250,000 people and costing over £11 billion a year. Historically they have often been overlooked by policy-makers, but they are well placed to play a central role in achieving many of the aims of NHS reform such as providing more personalised care closer to patients' homes, helping avoid unnecessary hospital admissions or shortening hospital stays, as well as leading efforts on preventive and wellness services.

A variety of staff and organisations provide a range of health services in the community.

Allied health professionals AHPs number over 82,500 and form a diverse group of statutory-registered practitioners who include art therapists, drama therapists, music therapists, chiropodists/podiatrists, dietitians, occupational therapists, orthoptists, orthotists and prosthetists, paramedics, physiotherapists, diagnostic radiographers, therapeutic radiographers and speech and language therapists. The DH has given AHPs the power to accept patients who refer themselves to AHP services.

Community nurses These include district nurses with a postgraduate qualification, registered nurses and nursing assistants. More than half the patients they see will be aged over 75. About half their work comes from GP referrals and a quarter from hospital staff; patients and carers can also refer themselves.

Community matrons As experienced nurses, community matrons use case management techniques with patients who make intensive use of healthcare to help them remain at home longer.

Health visitors These are qualified nurses or midwives with additional training and experience in child health, health promotion and education. Much of their work is with mothers and babies using a child-centred, family-focused approach, although they do provide more general health advice to people of all ages. Their support staff include nursery nurses and

children's health

Investment in children's and young people's health improves long-term outcomes, is cost-effective and reduces pressure on the NHS.

The profile of child health within the NHS in England has risen in recent years. Steps to strengthen a multi-disciplinary children's workforce and closer working between the NHS and local authorities – including schools and police – have led to improvements. Health service providers and staff are increasingly aware of their roles and responsibilities, such as safeguarding and the limits of confidentiality. The NHS has also started to engage and involve children and young people more in service delivery and commissioning.

Numerous reports demonstrate a national commitment to improving child physical and mental health and wellbeing. However, many of their recommendations have not been implemented. Sir Ian Kennedy's review of NHS services for children and young people in 2010 found considerable variation in quality, with many needing improvement and others being pockets of excellent practice. The NHS spends proportionally less on children's health services than on adult health services, and the UK lags behind Europe on key child health indicators.

The NHS reorganisation will significantly affect child health services. A number of different parts of the system will be responsible for commissioning those services. A 52-member Children and Young People's Forum, similar to the NHS Future Forum (see page 108), was set up at the beginning of 2012 to make recommendations for a children's and young people's outcomes strategy.

Further information

Getting it right for children and young people: overcoming cultural barriers in the NHS so as to meet their needs, DH, September 2010.

Children and young people's health – where next? NHS Confederation, Office for Public Management and Royal College of Paediatrics and Child Health, December 2011.

Involving children and young people in health services, NHS Confederation, Office for Public Management and Royal College of Paediatrics and Child Health, December 2011.

healthcare assistants, who focus on less complex family support and parenting skills. The Government intends to rejuvenate health visiting as a profession and recruit an extra 4,200 health visitors by 2015.

Midwives Generally attached to hospitals, but working in community settings.

Specialist nurses With expertise in stoma care, continence services, palliative care and support for people with long-term conditions.

A wide range of other health-related services come under the umbrella of community health:

School nursing – providing support and advice to schools on health issues, a role which has evolved considerably in recent years.

Community dentistry and dental public health – providing services to schools and people who are difficult to treat.

Podiatry – foot care for elderly people or those with diabetes, gait or lower limb problems. Independent contractors provide much of this care. More than half the service is for people aged over 65.

Physiotherapy – sometimes provided by GPs or hospitals in a community setting, with emphasis on rehabilitation.

Occupational therapy – providing advice, aids and adaptations. Some staff specialise in adults, some in children. The service is often provided by other agencies, such as local government, although in some cases the NHS provides local authority OT services.

Speech and language therapy – services for children and adults who have difficulty with communicating, eating, drinking or swallowing.

Clinical psychology – often provided by specialist mental health trusts, although more than 40 per cent of referrals come from general practice.

Family planning services – may cover sexual health problems as well as contraception, vasectomy and termination clinics and specialist clinics for young people.

Community rehabilitation – often for stroke or cardiac conditions. Services may be delivered by specialist teams in the patient's home or by combining intermediate care or community hospital care with home care.

Further information
A call to action: health visitor implementation plan summary progress report, DH, October 2011.

Integrated care

Integrated care involves health and social services working together. Demographic change means more people are living with long-term or multiple health problems: those with physical and learning disabilities, carers and multi-agency support for children all demand more integrated care, and there is an expectation that once-fragmented services can be coordinated to provide person-centred care that facilitates earlier and more cost-effective interventions. If the NHS reorganisation is to succeed, it will require some form of integration and more effective partnership working across all sectors.

On the front line, integrated care means GPs, community nurses, pharmacists, social care teams, ambulance services, schools and others working collaboratively with clear leadership, shared goals and shared information, and designing services around the needs of individuals and local communities.

Integration is especially important for continuing care, long-term care, intermediate care and end-of-life care, which – to be effective – all depend on a high degree of coordination between different organisations. Integration might involve bringing together different kinds of expertise and interventions – for example, by creating teams of primary and secondary care clinicians, or health and social care professionals.

The NHS Future Forum (see page 108) says that in order to accelerate service integration, commissioners should be able to override payment rules and share budgets with local authorities. It has also called for more explanation of how competition and choice can further – rather than hinder – integration, and warned that 'repeated structural change prescribed centrally' is a major barrier to integration.

Further information
Integration: a report from the NHS Future Forum, DH, January 2012.

Integrated care pilot programme

The DH launched a £4 million programme involving 16 pilots in 2009 to test different models of integrated care. The pilots are currently being evaluated on criteria such as health outcomes, quality of care, patient satisfaction, and effectiveness of relationships and systems. The sites involve partnerships of primary care with social care, secondary care, the voluntary and private sectors. Issues examined include dementia, care for the elderly, substance misuse, chronic obstructive pulmonary disease and end-of-life care. The methods involved include partnerships, new systems and care pathways that span primary, community, secondary and social care. The NHS Future Forum is also exploring the practical issues of creating a more integrated experience for patients, especially for frail elderly people with multiple long-term conditions, children with complex needs and adults with long-term mental health problems.

Further information

Integrated care pilots: an introductory guide, DH, September 2009.
Progress report: evaluation of the national integrated care pilots – June 2010, Ernst and Young, RAND Europe and DH, November 2010.

Continuing healthcare

Continuing healthcare is care provided over an extended period to someone aged 18 or over to meet physical and mental health needs that have arisen as a result of disability, accident or illness. The person may require services from the NHS and/or local authorities. Where they are assessed as having mainly health needs, the NHS will arrange and fund the complete package, which may be provided in any setting – hospital, hospice, home or care home. If they live in a care home, the NHS will contribute to their registered nursing care. Financial issues are not taken into account when deciding eligibility for NHS continuing healthcare. If a person does not qualify, the NHS may still have responsibility for contributing to a 'joint package' to meet their health needs.

About 53,000 people receive NHS continuing healthcare, costing £2 billion a year.

Further information

The national framework for NHS continuing healthcare and NHS-funded nursing care (revised), DH, July 2009.
NHS continuing healthcare practice guidance, DH, March 2010.
National framework for children and young people's continuing care, DH, March 2010.

Care for long-term conditions

More than 17.5 million people in the UK (15.4 million in England) suffer a long-term or chronic condition such as diabetes, asthma or arthritis. They represent 50 per cent of GP appointments, 64 per cent of outpatient appointments and A&E attendances, and 77 per cent of inpatient bed days. In total, they account for around 70 per cent of total health and social care spend, according to the DH. Numbers of people over 65 with a long-term condition are forecast to increase by 252 per cent by 2050.

Best practice requires early recognition, prompt diagnosis and treatment, early and specialist rehabilitation, equipment and accommodation and support for family and carers. For best quality care – and to maximise service efficiency – it is important that long-term conditions are effectively managed outside hospital wherever possible.

Health and social care organisations should assign 'community matrons' to the most vulnerable patients with complex multiple long-term conditions to monitor them, anticipate any problems and coordinate their care. Multi-professional teams should identify all people with a single serious long-term illness, assess their needs as early as possible and provide proactive care before their condition deteriorates. Everyone with a long-term condition should be educated about their health and encouraged to manage their own care more effectively.

Everyone with a long-term condition should be offered a personalised care plan. These address an individual's full range of needs, taking into account their health, personal, family, social, economic, educational, mental health, ethnic and cultural background and circumstances. The plan can be a written document or electronically recorded or recorded in the person's notes and accessible to them.

The DH has devised a 'generic long-term conditions model' that provides a structured approach to managing long-term conditions, matching care to need. It uses a risk prediction approach to identify people who most regularly use hospital services and are at risk of re-admissions, ranking them according to complexity of need. Commissioners can then use a range of interventions to meet their needs:

- case management – dedicated one-to-one support, for example from a community matron, with regular face-to-face contact

- personalised care planning – placing the person at the centre of decision-making about their care and agreeing a plan of how the care will be delivered
- support people to care for themselves (see page 76) – providing people with information and skills to make day-to-day decisions about the way they manage their health
- assistive technology – using telecare, telehealth technology and telephone coaching to support people to remain independent for as long as possible.

Further information
Long term health conditions 2011: research study conducted for the Department of Health, Ipsos MORI, April 2011.
Improving care for people with long term conditions: information sheet 1 – personalised care planning, an 'at a glance' guide for healthcare professionals, DH, November 2010.
National service framework for long-term conditions, DH, March 2005.

Key organisation
Expert Patients Programme CIC
A 2001 DH policy document, *The expert patient*, defined a new relationship between patient and professional, in which 'the era of the patient as the passive recipient of healthcare is changing and being replaced by a new emphasis on the relationship between the NHS and the people whom it serves'. Since then, many people have attended an 'expert patients programme' in England. The EPP is a free course of two-and-a-half hour sessions run over six weeks for people with chronic or long-term conditions that aims to give them the confidence to self-manage their health, while encouraging them to collaborate with health and social care professionals. Topics include healthy eating, dealing with pain and extreme tiredness, relaxation techniques and coping with feelings of depression.

Originally part of the NHS, the Expert Patients Programme has been a community interest company (CIC) since 2007. By the end of 2010, 80,000 people with long-term conditions had benefited from its courses.
www.expertpatients.co.uk

Self-care

The DH devised seven core principles of self-care to help health and social care staff support people with long-term conditions or complex needs to live independently and stay healthy. They are:

- ensure people can make informed choices to manage their self-care needs
- communicate effectively to enable people to assess their needs and gain confidence to care for themselves
- support and enable people to access appropriate information to manage their self-care
- support and enable individuals to develop skills in self-care
- support and enable individuals to use technology for self-care
- advise individuals how to access support networks and participate in planning, developing and evaluating services
- support and enable risk management and risk-taking to maximise independence and choice.

A networking and resource website, Self Care Connect, is run by the Expert Patients Programme for those with a professional interest in self-care.

The Self Care Forum was set up in 2011 with the aim of 'furthering the reach of self-care and embedding it into everyday life'. Members include patients, GPs, nurses, pharmacists, health service managers and the DH. The forum organises a national self-care week annually.

Further information
Improving care for people with long term conditions: information sheet 5 – what motivates people to self care, an 'at a glance' guide for healthcare professionals, DH, November 2010.
Self Care Connect **www.selfcareconnect.co.uk**
Self Care Forum **www.selfcareforum.org**

End-of-life care

Half a million people die in England each year, three-quarters after a chronic illness. Surveys show most people would prefer to die at home, although only 18 per cent do so; 58 per cent die in hospital, 17 per cent in care homes, 4 per cent in a hospice and 3 per cent elsewhere. End-of-life care is becoming more complex, with people living longer and the incidence of frailty and multiple conditions in older people rising. The DH therefore launched a ten-year end-of-life care strategy in 2008 to help more people to die in the setting they choose, promote dignity and respect, properly coordinate services and support carers.

It focuses on:
- improved community services, ensuring rapid-response community nursing services are available everywhere around the clock
- workforce training and development in assessing patients' and carers' needs and providing best-quality care
- developing specialist palliative care outreach services in the community, to support all adults regardless of their condition
- setting up a national end-of-life research initiative on how best to care for those at the end of their lives
- quality standards against which commissioners and providers can assess themselves and be assessed by regulators.

The National End-of-Life Care Programme aims to support implementation of the strategy by sharing good practice, and is backed with £286 million of government money.

Further information
End of life care strategy – promoting high quality care for all adults at the end of life, DH, July 2008.
Improving care for people with long term conditions: information sheet 8 – end of life care and personalised care planning, an 'at a glance' guide for healthcare professionals, DH, November 2010.
National End-of-Life Care Programme **www.endoflifecareforadults.nhs.uk**

Secondary care

The changing role of hospitals
Acute hospitals have always dominated healthcare spending and provision, but their role has begun to change fundamentally. Demographic, economic and technological changes are fuelling a drive to use community settings for some services traditionally provided in hospitals, in a way that emphasises support for health and wellbeing rather than simply curing disease.

Changes in the last two decades have revolutionised surgery: lasers and 'keyhole' techniques have led to quicker recovery and less risk of infection. Procedures that previously required long stays in hospital, such as hernia operations, can now be done as day cases more locally. New drugs have made some surgery, such as treatment for stomach ulcers, completely unnecessary. Eighty per cent of all surgery could be done locally, leaving the most complex 20 per cent for specialist centres with the most highly skilled surgeons using the latest technology.

Older people are the main users of the NHS: although they make up about a fifth of the population, they occupy two-thirds of hospital beds, and are three times more likely to be admitted to hospital.

Reports suggest older people do not always receive the same standard of care from the NHS as younger patients. But since the Equality Act 2010 came into force in April 2012, arbitrary and harmful age discrimination in the NHS has been banned, including:
- making assumptions about whether an older patient should be referred for treatment based solely on their age, rather than on their individual need and fitness
- not referring certain age groups for a particular treatment that is considered mainly – but not exclusively – for working-age adults
- not considering the wellbeing or dignity of older people.

Commissioners and providers of NHS and social care services may continue to make clinically justifiable decisions based on age for relevant services such as eligibility for screening and vaccination programmes. The Act aims to prevent only harmful discrimination, not discrimination for which there are beneficial or justifiable reasons.

There are currently 650,000 people with dementia in England, and by 2025 over 1 million people in the UK will be living with dementia. The National Audit Office estimates that dementia costs health and social care services £8.2 billion a year. Alzheimer's Research UK puts the overall cost of dementia to society as a whole at £23 billion a year. It is estimated that £80 million a year could be saved by improving hospital care for people with dementia and that every general hospital has excess costs of £6 million because of the condition, due to worse outcomes for length of stay, mortality and institutionalisation.

More than two-thirds of hospital staff do not believe they have had sufficient training to deliver quality care to people with dementia, according to the National Audit of Dementia. It also found half of staff had insufficient training in communicating with people with dementia, and 54 per cent had not had enough training in dealing with challenging behaviour. Only 15 per cent of wards used colour schemes to help people with dementia find their way around. The National Audit of Dementia is working with hospitals to measure criteria known to impact on people admitted with dementia, such as involvement of carers, discharge planning and identified changes to support needs during admission.

The DH has produced a dementia commissioning pack to help design cost-effective services suited to local needs. It supports planning from early diagnosis to end-of-life care, and includes guidance on how to reduce the inappropriate use of antipsychotic medication. It was developed in consultation with health and social care experts, including people with dementia and their carers.

The Care Quality Commission carried out unannounced inspections of 100 NHS hospitals in 2011 to assess whether older people were treated with dignity and respect and whether they were given food and drink to meet their needs. It found 20 hospitals failing on one or both criteria.

Further information

Delivering Dignity: Securing dignity in care for older people in hospitals and care homes. A report for consultation, NHS Confederation, Local Government Association and Age UK, February 2012.

Improving dementia services in England – an interim report, NAO, January 2010.

Dignity and nutrition inspection programme: national overview, CQC, October 2011.

Report of the National Audit of Dementia Care in General Hospitals 2011, Healthcare Quality Improvement Partnership, December 2011.

Dementia Information Portal **www.dementia.dh.gov.uk**

Meanwhile, patient choice, payment by results and the reorganisation of commissioning are affecting the balance of power between organisations, stimulating further change – especially as value for money has become even more important with the slowdown in spending.

The result of these developments is that the traditional model of the district general hospital is changing. Local hospitals are likely to remain important, but rather than working in isolation will have to collaborate with other providers and each other as part of 'multi-hospital networks of care'. Rather than exercising local monopolies, hospitals will need to promote competition and choice.

Spotlight on policy: personal health budgets

Personal health budgets are designed to enhance independence and choice for people receiving care or support. A personal budget combines resources from different funding streams into a single sum. The purpose is to give people a clear idea of the finance available and enable them to make their own decisions about their care – for example, by having someone support them at home rather than going into residential care. The care plan – setting out the individual's health and social care needs, desired outcomes, money available and how it will be spent – is at the heart of the personal health budget. Those receiving budgets include older people, people with learning disabilities, physical disabilities and/or sensory impairments and mental health service users.

Personal budgets were originally developed for social care and ruled out for NHS adoption in 2006 amid fears they would compromise the founding principle that care should be free at the point of need. They were eventually piloted for healthcare from 2009. Current pilots cover 2,700 people across 20 sites. On the recommendation of the NHS Future Forum (see page 108), the coalition Government intends to begin a national roll-out once the evaluation of the pilots is complete in October 2012. People receiving continuing healthcare (see page 73) will be the first to have a right to ask for a personal health budget, by April 2014.

Personal budgets took three forms in the pilots:
• a notional budget held by a commissioner, such as a doctor or PCT
• a budget managed on an individual's behalf by a third party, such as a charity
• a direct cash payment made to an individual and managed by them.

Research shows local leaders, clinicians, service users and carers all support the aims that personal budgets are designed to achieve. They could potentially create a step-change in innovation and responsiveness in the NHS, but radically alter how the health service works. They may have an impact on health inequalities across the population if take-up is greatest among patients who are more articulate or have relatively better health. Research suggests personal health budgets are likely to be attractive to a significant minority – but not the majority – of NHS patients. Continuing to provide existing services to the many who wish to stay, while funding personal budgets for patients choosing to go elsewhere, will present a considerable problem to local commissioners and providers. In the long term, personal health budgets may increase costs.

Further information

Shaping personal health budgets: a view from the top, NHS Confederation/National Mental Health Development Unit, December 2009.

Facing up to the challenge of personal health budgets, NHS Confederation/National Mental Health Development Unit, March 2011.

Personal health budgets: the views of service users and carers, NHS Confederation/National Mental Health Development Unit, August 2011.

Personal health budgets: early experiences of budget holders – fourth interim report, DH, October 2011.

Briefing 222: Personal health budgets: countdown to roll-out, NHS Confederation, October 2011.

Personal health budgets and NHS continuing healthcare: discussion paper, DH, January 2012.

Personal Health Budgets Learning Network **www.personalhealthbudgets.dh.gov.uk**

Change to local health services is often controversial for staff and the public, who need to be involved in developing plans from early on. The DH's National Clinical Advisory Team provides a pool of clinical experts to guide the local NHS on service change proposals to ensure they are safe and accessible for patients. Before consulting the public, proposals should be subject to independent clinical and management assessment. Since 2008 this has been conducted under the Office of Government Commerce's gateway review process. It comprises a series of short reviews carried out

Vital statistics: mean length of hospital stay (days)

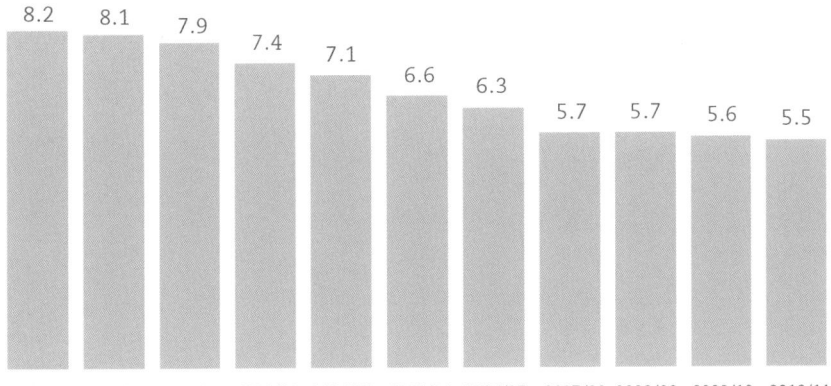

2000/01	2001/02	2002/03	2003/04	2004/05	2005/06	2006/07	2007/08	2008/09	2009/10	2010/11
8.2	8.1	7.9	7.4	7.1	6.6	6.3	5.7	5.7	5.6	5.5

Source: The Health and Social Care Information Centre, *Hospital Episode Statistics*

Independent Reconfiguration Panel
Set up in 2003, the IRP advises the Secretary of State on proposals for
changes to NHS services that have been contested locally. It also offers
advice to the NHS, local authorities and others on NHS reconfiguration
issues.

The local authority health overview and scrutiny committee (see page 149)
may refer a proposal if it is not satisfied:
• with the content of the consultation or the time allowed
• with the reasons given for not carrying out consultation
• that the proposal is in the interests of the health service locally.

Although the IRP is a last resort when other options for local resolution
have been explored, it welcomes early informal contact to avoid formal
referral if possible. Once a case is accepted, the chair agrees any specific
terms of reference and a timetable for reporting. The chair will normally
appoint a subgroup of three (one health professional, one health manager,
one patient and citizen representative) to consider the case. The IRP
encourages locally acceptable solutions. Its advice takes account of public
and patient involvement and the rigour of local consultation. As a non-
departmental public body, the IRP offers advice only: final decisions rest
with the Secretary of State.

Further information
Learning from reviews: an overview, third edition, IRP, December 2010.
www.irpanel.org.uk

at key stages and designed to highlight risks which could threaten a
project's success. The review usually takes three to four days and involves
interviewing clinicians, patients, users, boards, staff and managers.

In addition, the Secretary of State introduced four key tests for proposed
service changes in May 2010. Proposals must demonstrate:
• support from clinical commissioners
• strengthened public and patient engagement
• clarity on the clinical evidence base
• consistency with current and prospective patient choice.

These tests are designed to ensure service changes are driven by local
clinicians, patients and their representatives.

Treatment centres

Treatment centres are units that carry out planned surgery and treatment in areas that have traditionally had the longest waiting times, separating them from unplanned care and so lessening the risk that operations have to be cancelled. The DH looked to them to create innovation, increase productivity and rapidly expand capacity. They have developed new staff roles, including perioperative specialist practitioners, advanced nurse practitioners/advisers and healthcare assistant technicians in radiology, ophthalmology and surgery.

A treatment centre's essential features include:
- delivering a high volume of routine treatments and/or diagnostics
- streamlined services using defined pathways
- planned and booked services, with emphasis on patient choice and convenience.

Treatment centres have developed on two models. Some are run by the NHS, others by the independent sector under contract to the NHS (see page 27). They may be:
- virtual treatment centres – defined services within an existing hospital, using care pathways to ensure efficiency and enhance the patient's experience
- stand-alone new-build treatment centres – purposely designed for maximum efficiency and to ensure the best patient flows
- refurbished sites – possibly using surplus estate to give quick access to suitable buildings.

The type of work they do falls into three categories:
- short-stay inpatient work, often in a single specialty such as orthopaedics or ophthalmology
- day-case or outpatient work
- community-based diagnostic work, such as endoscopy and ultrasound, and minor surgical procedures such as excision of cysts and lesions, and vasectomies.

Centres may care for patients within a single specialty or a range of specialties.

Urgent and emergency care

The system for delivering urgent and emergency care includes:

- NHS Direct
- community pharmacies and self-care
- GP services, including out-of-hours services (see page 63)
- urgent care centres, including walk-in centres and minor injuries units (see page 66)
- ambulance services
- hospital A&E departments
- critical care services.

Urgent care is for patients who have an injury or illness that requires immediate attention but is not usually serious enough to require a visit to an A&E department.

Emergency care underwent major changes after the launch of a ten-year strategy, Reforming Emergency Care, in 2001. The strategy was based on six key principles:

- services should be designed from the patient's point of view
- patients should receive a consistent response wherever, whenever and however they contact the service
- patients' needs should be met by the professional best able to help them
- information from each stage of the patient's journey should be shared with other professionals involved in their care
- assessment or treatment should not be delayed through the absence of diagnostic or specialist advice
- clear and measurable standards should be applied to emergency care.

The strategy aimed to transform the patient's experience of emergency care through shorter waits, faster response times, better training and equipment and a more integrated approach to emergency and critical care.

In 2008, the Healthcare Commission (forerunner of the Care Quality Commission, see page 147) found 'significant improvements' in emergency and urgent care had been achieved as a result of services such as NHS Direct and NHS walk-in centres, faster ambulance response times and shorter waits in A&E. This was despite an increase in numbers using A&E and urgent care centres.

NHS Direct

NHS Direct is a 24-hour telephone health advice and information service staffed by nurses. It provides callers to its helpline with information on

111 – the national number for non-emergency care

A new, free telephone service, available by dialling 111, is providing access to urgent but non-emergency healthcare in the same way the existing 999 service enables instant access to emergency care. Currently being piloted, it will be extended nationally by April 2013.

Available 24 hours a day, the 111 service assesses callers' needs and provides clinical advice or information, or routes them to a local service such as a walk-in centre or minor injuries unit. If a caller needs to see a nurse or needs an urgent home visit in the middle of the night, NHS 111 will organise that. In the event of a caller needing emergency treatment, an ambulance is sent without the need for further assessment.

NHS 111 content is being made available online, including health information, checklists of symptoms and a directory of local services. A mobile phone app will offer the same services. GPs will be able to link their own booking systems to 111, allowing their patients to book an urgent appointment. The service is staffed by call advisers, supported by nurses.

Further information

Evaluation of NHS 111 pilot sites: second interim report, University of Sheffield/DH, October 2011.

what to do if they or their family are feeling ill, advice on particular health conditions, details of local healthcare services, such as doctors, dentists or late-night pharmacies, as well as self-help and support organisations. Staff use a computer-based decision-support system to suggest the best course of action, and can pass calls directly to emergency services; about 3 per cent of calls are emergencies.

Launched in 1998, NHS Direct employs 3,150 staff, of whom 1,150 are nurses. Its 30 contact centres around the country handle 23,000 calls every day. The top symptoms people call about are abdominal pain, dental tooth/jaw pain, rashes, medicine enquiries and chest pain. NHS Direct says that in 2010/11, patients' use of its services meant that 1.1 million A&E attendances or 999 calls, 1.6 million GP consultations and 500,000 other face-to-face appointments were avoided; 55 per cent of calls are completed without referral.

NHS Direct also offers services to other parts of the health service, including:
- out-of-hours support for GPs and dental services
- telephone support for patients with long-term conditions
- pre- and post-operative support for patients
- 24-hour response to health scares
- remote clinics via telephone.

NHS Direct in England and Wales operate from the same telephone number: 0845 4647. When the 111 service is launched nationally, this number will be decommissioned, though NHS Direct says it 'intends to have a new role as a major provider of NHS 111, competing with other organisations to deliver the service regionally'. Scotland's information service is called NHS 24 and uses 08454 242424.

NHS Direct Online

NHS Direct Online (www.nhsdirect.nhs.uk) is an interactive website that provides:
- a self-help guide to treating common problems at home
- a health encyclopaedia with over 400 topics
- personal responses to specific requests for information
- a searchable database of hospitals and community health services, GPs, dentists, opticians and pharmacies.

Visits to NHS Direct Online numbered more than 5.6 million in 2010/11. The service is also available via the NHS Choices website (see page 205).

Ambulance services

Ambulance services have changed significantly in the past decade, with big improvements in response times for 999 calls, in training and quality of care, vehicle standards, equipment and technology. As demand for ambulances has risen steadily every year, ambulance services have developed to provide more diagnosis, treatment and care in people's homes, helping avoid unnecessary A&E admissions.

NHS ambulances in England received 7.87 million urgent and emergency calls in 2009/10 – 391,000 more than the previous year – of which 6.42 million resulted in an emergency response vehicle arriving on the scene. In many areas ambulance trusts also provide transport to get patients to hospital for non-emergency treatment.

Ambulance trust areas

Source: Department of Health

In addition to transporting patients, ambulance services now have a multiplicity of roles:

- helping patients access the most appropriate NHS services – call handlers must assess emergency calls and redirect callers to other services if necessary, as many people dial 999 unaware of how to access more appropriate non-emergency services
- taking care to the patient, not always taking the patient to hospital – only 70 per cent of patients treated by the ambulance service are taken to A&E, with the remainder often treated at home by paramedics
- promoting public health – including provision of first-aid training to local industry and campaigns raising awareness of the symptoms of serious illnesses
- preventing accidents – particularly reducing falls among older people by working with social care services

- safeguarding vulnerable children and adults – more than any other NHS service, ambulance crews operate in people's homes and have developed processes to ensure the right agencies receive the right referral, with all information treated confidentially and sensitively
- working with the local community – for example, by training local first responders to provide life-saving treatment like defibrillation while an ambulance is on its way, especially in rural areas.

Crews now use satellite navigation systems, and emergency ambulances are equipped with technology such as ECG machines and telemetry, which lets crews send information about a patient's condition directly to the receiving hospital. Services deploy solo responders, such as motorcycles and rapid-response vehicles, to travel through heavy traffic more easily. In 2010, ambulance services contracted, leased or owned 30 air ambulances, which flew 19,000 missions and served 177 A&E departments.

Ambulance services are improving their ability to assess, diagnose and treat patients over the telephone and face-to-face. For example, new critical care paramedics – authorised to use pain-relief drugs and with enhanced resuscitation skills – are improving care for critically ill and injured patients. Emergency care practitioners (ECPs) assess, diagnose and treat minor illnesses and injuries in the community or in people's homes, helping reduce unnecessary A&E admissions. ECPs also support GPs in and out of hours by making home visits. In parts of the country, ambulance services coordinate a single point of access to urgent care, ensuring patients get the most appropriate services for their clinical need.

Key organisation: **Ambulance Service Network**
The Ambulance Service Network (ASN) was established as part of the NHS Confederation to provide a strong and independent voice for UK ambulance services, and to foster a closer working relationship with the rest of the NHS and other stakeholders in health and social care. The ASN has 18 members – 11 English NHS ambulance trusts, Northern Ireland, Wales and the islands of Guernsey, Jersey and Isle of Man. There are two associate members including the Association of Air Ambulances and the Scottish Ambulance Service.
www.nhsconfed.org/asn

New key standards for ambulance services were implemented in 2011, taking account of quality and outcomes as well as response times. The response time targets are:

- 75 per cent of category A (immediately life-threatening) calls should receive a response within eight minutes – whether by traditional ambulance, car, motorbike or volunteer community responder
- if a category A patient requires transport, it should arrive within 19 minutes of the request being made, 95 per cent of the time.

The 11 new quality standards include:

- patients eligible for primary angioplasty following a heart attack receiving the treatment within 150 minutes
- suspected stroke patients, assessed face-to-face, arriving at a hyperacute stroke centre within 60 minutes.

Further information
Factsheet: Seeing ambulance services in a different light – more than a patient transport service, Ambulance Service Network/NHS Confederation, June 2010.
Critical care paramedics – delivering enhanced pre-hospital trauma and resuscitation care: a cost-effective approach, SDO Network/Ambulance Service Network/NHS Confederation, March 2011.
Transforming NHS ambulance services: forty-sixth report of session 2010–12, House of Commons public accounts committee, September 2011.
Briefing 226: An involving service – ambulance responses in urban and rural areas, Ambulance Service Network/NHS Confederation, November 2011.

Accident and emergency
About 20 million visits are made to A&E departments in England every year, and about one-fifth result in admissions to hospital as emergencies. Before a patient is admitted for further care, transferred or discharged, there can often be a lengthy chain of decisions, tests and treatment that can be subject to delay. From 2004 until 2011 A&E departments had a target of seeing, diagnosing and treating all patients within four hours of their arrival: by 2010/11, 97.4 per cent of patients were seen within this target. This has now been replaced with a range of considerations to reflect timeliness and effectiveness of treatment – and overall patient experience – rather than focus solely on faster care. These include:

- unplanned re-attendance
- left without being seen
- total time spent in A&E
- time to initial assessment
- time to treatment.

Further information

A&E clinical quality indicators: implementation guidance, DH, December 2010.

Trauma services

Major trauma – severe injury including head injury – is the main cause of death in people under 40 and a cause of long-term disability. As it constitutes only a small proportion of acute activity – on average about two per hospital per week – it historically received relatively little management and planning attention. A series of critical reports from the Royal Colleges, the National Confidential Inquiry into Patient Outcome and Death and the National Audit Office, showed that services were inadequate. An estimated 450 to 600 lives could be saved in NHS hospitals every year if trauma services were better organised.

Therefore the NHS is establishing regional networks of major trauma centres to ensure patients with serious and life-threatening injuries are treated quickly in a specialist hospital. The first, the London Regional Trauma Network, began in 2010. Around 20 major trauma centres are being set up in England as part of the programme. The centres offer a full range of trauma specialists, including orthopaedics, neurosurgery and radiology teams. Care is led by a trauma consultant available 24 hours a day. Many patients need a personalised rehabilitation programme taking many months and involving physiotherapists, occupational and speech therapists, either at the major trauma centre or other units in the area.

A national clinical director was appointed in 2009, and £20 million has been invested in the National Institute of Health Research Centre for Surgical Reconstruction and Microbiology at the Queen Elizabeth Hospital, Birmingham. Research will focus initially on the most urgent challenges in trauma including:
• identifying effective resuscitation techniques
• surgical care after multiple injuries or amputation
• fighting wound infections.

Research highlighted by the NHS Confederation and Ambulance Service Network shows that while trauma networks can improve outcomes, creating a network is only the start. Planners in NHS regions and their advisers centrally must take into account the uncertainties in the evidence about how to improve outcomes and not try to implement uniform systems based on received wisdom. The NHS needs to acknowledge the public value of the 'rule of rescue' – the principle that health services have a duty to save endangered lives. But while improvements may be cost-effective and even pay dividends for society in the longer term, no evidence suggests this will lead to net savings for health economies and the NHS should not plan on that assumption.

Further information
Major trauma care in England, NAO, February 2010.
Implementing trauma systems: key issues for the NHS, Ambulance Service Network/NHS Confederation, August 2010.
London Trauma Office **www.londontraumaoffice.nhs.uk**
Trauma Audit and Research Network **www.tarn.ac.uk**

Critical care
Critical care comprises intensive and high-dependence care services. During the past decade a modernisation programme for critical care has integrated services for critically ill patients wherever they are in the health system. Key objectives were to:
• increase capacity
• develop services supporting critically ill patients throughout the hospital – not necessarily restricted to critical care 'units'
• provide an integrated critical care organisation within and between hospitals working in collaborative networks
• provide comprehensive information and data on critical care.

Critical care is provided to more than 300,000 patients annually in England. The number of adult critical care beds in November 2011 was 3,702, with an occupancy rate of 84.3 per cent. There were 393 paediatric critical care beds, of which 85 per cent were occupied and 1,295 neonatal critical care beds, of which 76.3 per cent were occupied.

Maternity services
The NHS is striving to offer a wider choice of type and place of maternity care and birth. Services should be accessible to all women and be designed to take full account of their individual needs, including different language, cultural, religious and social needs or particular needs related to disability, including learning disability.

Four national 'choice guarantees' were introduced in 2009 so that all women can choose:
• how to access maternity care – by going straight to a midwife or a GP
• type of antenatal care – either midwifery or care provided by a team of maternity health professionals, including midwives and obstetricians

- place of birth – either at home, supported by a midwife; in a local midwifery unit or birth centre, which might be in the community or in a hospital, supported by a midwife; or in a hospital supported by a maternity team that may include midwives, obstetricians, paediatricians and anaesthetists
- postnatal care – either at home or in a community setting, such as a Sure Start children's centre.

The coalition Government has proposed extending maternity choice in pre-conception, antenatal and postnatal care. It suggests maternity service providers should work together as networks to extend choice and improve quality.

The NHS Choices website (see page 205) now includes a maternity comparison tool with information on maternity units, making it easier for expectant women to compare local services, quality of care and other facilities such as car parking. Users can rate and comment on their maternity services and read about others' experiences.

Further information
Maternity matters: choice, access and continuity of care in a safe service, DH, April 2007.
Liberating the NHS: greater choice and control – a consultation on proposals, DH, October 2010.

Mental health
At least one in four people will experience a mental health problem at some point in their life, and one in six adults has a mental health problem at any one time. Almost half of all adults will experience at least one episode of depression during their lifetime, while about one in 100 people has a severe mental illness. One in ten children aged between five and 16 years has a mental health problem. Mental health services absorb about 14 per cent of the NHS budget, while the number of consultant psychiatrists, clinical psychologists and mental health nurses has risen significantly in the last 15 years.

Today, the principles guiding mental healthcare are:
- care provided closer to home
- earlier intervention
- 24/7 home treatment
- care tailored to individuals' needs
- better access to modern drugs
- care provided by multi-disciplinary teams
- more use of talking therapies.

Further information
Factsheet: Key facts and trends in mental health – updated figures and statistics, Mental Health Network/NHS Confederation, September 2011.

Organising mental health services
Mental health services are provided as part of primary and secondary care by the NHS, social care and the independent and voluntary sectors. Provision comprises acute inpatient care, community and rehabilitation services, residential care centres, day hospitals and drop-in centres. About 80,000 staff work in statutory mental health services, and 1.2 million people are in contact with mental health services annually.

Primary and community services
Of people who receive help for mental health problems – whether for depression, anxiety or other mental disorders, or for a psychotic illness such as schizophrenia – 90 per cent are dealt with in primary care: 30 per cent of GP consultations have a significant mental health component.

Nevertheless, more than 60 per cent of NHS spending on adult mental health is devoted to acute inpatient services. Less than half of GPs have postgraduate training in psychiatry and only 2 per cent of practice nurses have mental health training, although about half of GP surgeries provide counselling. GPs usually refer patients they cannot help directly to the local community mental health team (CMHT) or to a psychiatric outpatient clinic.

CMHTs are the main source of specialist support for those suffering severe and enduring mental health problems. They assess and monitor mental health needs using two systems – the care programme approach or care management. These require that everyone seen by specialist mental health services should have their need for treatment assessed, a care plan drawn up and a named mental health worker to coordinate their care, including a regular review of their needs. They aim to help provide continuity of care across different services, promote multi-professional and inter-agency working, and ensure appropriate care for people diagnosed with serious mental illness on discharge from hospital.

CMHT members include community psychiatric nurses, social workers, psychologists, occupational therapists, doctors and support workers. Patients will regularly meet the psychiatrist from their mental health team at a psychiatric outpatient clinic for review of their treatment.

Spotlight on policy: a new mental health strategy

A cross-government, all-age strategy for mental health in England was published in early 2011. *No health without mental health* stresses the Government's expectation that there be 'parity of esteem' between mental and physical health services. It has two underlying aims:
• to improve mental health and wellbeing and keep people well
• to improve outcomes through high-quality services equally accessible to all.

In line with the *Liberating the NHS* white paper, the Government says it is devolving power to localities, so the strategy is not intended to be directive: local services should be free to innovate and design their own services. The strategy sets out six objectives:
• more people will have good mental health
• more people with mental health problems will recover
• more people with mental health problems will have good physical health
• more people will have a positive experience of care and support
• fewer people will suffer avoidable harm
• fewer people will experience stigma and discrimination.

The strategy confirms that mental health is to move towards payment by results (see page 162). A ministerial advisory group of key stakeholders, including people with mental health problems and carers, will help with implementation. The strategy also includes commitments to:
• agree and use a new national measure of wellbeing
• challenge stigma
• ensure that by 2014 people in contact with the criminal justice system will have improved access to mental health services
• launch a set of 'recovery' pilots to test the key features of organisational practice to support the recovery of those using mental health services.

A suicide-prevention strategy has also been published.

Further information
No health without mental health: a cross-government mental health outcomes strategy for people of all ages, HM Government, February 2011.
No health without mental health: delivering better mental health outcomes for people of all ages, HM Government, February 2011.
Briefing 216: No health without mental health – the new strategy for mental health in England, Mental Health Network/NHS Confederation, February 2011.
Consultation on preventing suicide in England: a cross-government outcomes strategy to save lives, HM Government, July 2011.

Providing mental health services in the community has prompted new approaches to care to avoid hospital admission. For example:

- early intervention teams aim to treat psychotic illness as quickly and effectively as possible, especially during the critical period after its onset
- assertive outreach teams provide intensive support for severely mentally ill people who are difficult to engage in more traditional services
- home treatment and crisis resolution teams provide flexible acute care in patients' own homes with a 24-hour service to help with crises.

The availability of 'talking treatments' is being extended through the Improving Access to Psychological Therapies (IAPT) programme. Set up in 2006, the programme comprises:

- cognitive behavioural therapy (CBT)
- counselling for depression
- interpersonal psychotherapy
- couples therapy
- dynamic interpersonal psychotherapy.

IAPT is encouraging provision outside hospital, in people's homes, GP practices, Job Centres and other community settings. Between 2008 and 2010, 491,000 people started treatment, over 282,000 completed it, 95,000 moved to recovery, with many more experiencing significant improvement in their symptoms. By 2011, 3,660 new CBT workers had been trained, and the Government announced plans to make IAPT available to all adults over the next four years as well as extending it to children and young people.

The Care Quality Commission's annual survey of community mental health patients found most had not spent any time in hospital over the last 12 months, underlining the importance of community services. The vast majority said they were listened to carefully, treated with respect and dignity and had trust and confidence in their health or social care worker. But although 42 per cent had experienced the care programme approach – which should include housing, employment and financial advice – 35 per cent had not received any help with finding or keeping work, 27 per cent had not received any help with finding or keeping accommodation and 27 per cent had not been given any help with financial advice or benefits.

Further information

Talking therapies: a four year plan of action, DH, February 2011.
Briefing 217: Talking therapies: a four-year plan of action, Mental Health Network/NHS Confederation, April 2011.

Briefing 219: Early intervention in psychosis services, Mental Health Network/NHS Confederation, May 2011.
Community mental health survey 2011, CQC, August 2011.
Research digest 2: New service models in mental health: emerging lessons, SDO Network/NHS Confederation, December 2011.

Hospital services

Psychiatric hospital services have been progressively scaled down over the past 30 years, as many services are now provided in the community. Admissions fell 17 per cent between 2004 and 2009, though they rose by 5.1 per cent the following year. Numbers of patients detained under the Mental Health Act have been rising, intensifying pressure on beds and stress on staff: in 2009/10 they rose 3.5 per cent to 49,417. One result has been a significant increase in pressure on hospital services, with psychiatric beds experiencing high occupancy rates – 29 per cent of wards exceeded capacity in 2009/10. Acute inpatient services deal mainly with patients suffering severe mental illness.

A Care Quality Commission survey in 2009 found that although 85 per cent of patients said they were made to feel welcome when they were admitted to hospital, 'too great a proportion' felt let down by aspects of their care: only 45 per cent said they always felt safe on the ward, and less than half who wanted talking therapies received any.

Further information

National NHS patient survey programme: mental health acute inpatient service users survey 2009, CQC, September 2009.

Child and adolescent mental health services

One in ten children has a clinically significant mental health problem. At any one time, more than a million children will have a diagnosable mental health disorder, and mental illness in childhood and adolescence costs up to £59,000 per child every year. Child and adolescent mental health services (CAMHS) cater for those with all types of mental disorder, including hyperkinetic disorders. Services are arranged into four tiers, which should be closely linked:

• tier 1 includes services contributing to mental healthcare of children and young people, but whose primary function is not mental healthcare (for example, schools and GPs)
• tier 2 includes mental health professionals assessing and treating those who do not respond at tier 1

- tier 3 includes teams of mental health professionals providing multi-disciplinary interventions for more complex problems
- tier 4 includes the most severe and complex problems that cannot be dealt with at tier 3, including inpatient and specialist services such as eating disorders.

NHS and foundation trusts are the principal providers of CAMHS, although local authorities and the independent sector also provide services. Since 2006 all areas have been required to have 'comprehensive CAMHS', including out-of-hours emergency cover as well as adequate provision for all young people up to age 18 with mental health problems. However, many are still far from meeting this requirement.

The Government is investing in psychological therapies (see page 95), including talking therapies, for children and young people. It has also asked universities and teaching providers to link up with local CAMHS partnerships to help improve services.

Forensic services

Forensic mental health services deal with mentally ill people who may need a degree of physical security and have shown challenging behaviour beyond the scope of general psychiatric services. Some may be mentally disordered offenders.

Services fall into three categories:
- low-security services tend to be based near general psychiatric wards in NHS hospitals, and are for people detained under the Mental Health Act who pose a level of risk or challenge so cannot be treated in open settings

- medium-secure services often operate regionally and are provided by NHS and independent sector organisations; they usually consist of locked wards with a greater number and a wider range of staff, and patients – who may have a history of offending or have been transferred from prison or court – typically remain in treatment between two and five years
- high-security services are provided by the three special hospitals (Ashworth, Broadmoor and Rampton), which have much greater levels of security and care for people who pose an immediate and serious risk to others.

In addition, new services are developing to meet the needs of mentally disordered offenders in the community. A strategic advisory body, the National Oversight Group, advises on policy development, commissioning and performance management for high-secure services in England and Wales, taking into account the needs of the wider NHS and the criminal justice system.

Further information
National Oversight Group annual report 2010–11, DH, December 2011.

Revising mental health law: the Mental Health Act 2007

The Mental Health Act 2007 updates the Mental Health Act 1983 through seven major amendments, while an eighth amendment updates the Mental Capacity Act 2005. These provide better safeguards for service users, with new rights to advocacy, a say in who their nearest relative is and the right to refuse electro-convulsive therapy and other treatments.

The amendments include:
- a simplified definition of mental disorder
- a wider definition of medical treatment
- the introduction of supervised community treatment after initial detention and treatment in hospital
- additional safeguards for service users
- changes to professional roles to allow a wider range of staff to adopt the functions traditionally delivered by approved social workers and medical professionals
- improved access to review tribunals
- abolition of finite restriction orders.

Care for special groups

Healthcare for people with learning disabilities

There are 985,000 people in England with a learning disability – 2 per cent of the population – and numbers will increase significantly in the next 15 years, especially among older age groups. But only 177,000 are known to use learning disability services. People with learning disabilities have greater health needs than the general population, being more likely to experience mental illness and more prone to chronic health problems such as epilepsy and cerebral palsy. They are also 58 times more likely to die before the age of 50. But many have difficulty accessing healthcare and are less likely to seek routine screening. All too often they have been effectively invisible to mainstream NHS services.

When they do access health services they may be subject to 'diagnostic overshadowing' bias – clinicians' tendency to overlook symptoms of mental health problems among people with learning disabilities, attributing them to the disability. Therefore, people with learning disabilities may need support when using mainstream services, including longer appointments and help with communication.

The 2001 learning disability white paper, *Valuing people*, was based on four key principles that still apply:
- legal and civil rights – people with learning disabilities have the right to a decent education, to grow up to vote, marry and have a family, and express their opinions, with help and support where necessary
- independence – individuals' needs will differ, but the presumption should be one of independence rather than dependence, with public services providing the support needed to maximise this
- choice – everyone should be able to make choices, including people with severe and profound disabilities, with help and support
- inclusion – people with learning disabilities should be able to do ordinary things, make use of mainstream services and be fully included in the local community.

Despite progress after the white paper, the 2008 Michael Inquiry found much remained to be done and a follow-up white paper, *Valuing people now*, set out plans for addressing the inquiry's recommendations. Priorities included:
- increasing the range of housing options for people with learning disabilities and their families

- ensuring all local authority services and developments for people with learning disabilities and their carers are underpinned by person-centred planning
- increasing employment opportunities.

Valuing people now remains the national policy for people with learning disabilities, and by the end of 2010 the Government claimed improvements included more people having an annual health check, moving into their own homes from residential campuses and finding jobs.

A National Learning Disabilities Programme Board, chaired by the care services minister, monitors progress and links to regional learning disability boards and, through them, to all local partnership boards. Local partnership boards were set up after 2001 to bring together relevant local agencies and stakeholders, giving a voice to people with learning disabilities and their carers. In practice, their membership, governance, responsibilities, accountability and effectiveness have varied, with few operating as envisaged: most have focused on process and engagement rather than improving outcomes. Nevertheless, they are crucial to achieving the aims of *Valuing people now*.

The Ombudsman highlighted several cases in 2009 – thought not to be isolated incidents – where health and social care failings had led to the premature and avoidable deaths of people with learning disabilities. The Ombudsman recommended all NHS and social care organisations urgently review their effectiveness and capacity for helping people with learning disabilities.

The DH has issued revised guidance to the NHS on safeguarding vulnerable adults to help NHS commissioners, health service managers and practitioners prevent and respond to neglect and abuse.

Following a BBC *Panorama* programme in May 2011, uncovering details of systematic abuse of patients by staff in Winterbourne View, an independent hospital in Gloucestershire for people with learning disabilities and challenging behaviour, the Care Quality Commission launched unannounced inspections of 150 services that provide care for people with learning disabilities, expected to be completed in 2012. The DH is also carrying out its own review.

Further information

Valuing people: a new strategy for learning disability for the 21st century, DH, March 2001.
Healthcare for all: report of the independent inquiry into access to healthcare for people with learning disabilities, DH, July 2008.
Valuing people now: a new three-year strategy for people with learning disabilities, HM Government, January 2009.
Six lives: the provision of public services to people with learning disabilities, Parliamentary and Health Service Ombudsman, March 2009.
Six lives progress report, DH, October 2010.
Valuing people now: summary report March 2009–September 2010, DH, December 2010.
People with learning disabilities in England 2010, Learning Disabilities Observatory, January 2011.
Safeguarding adults: role of managers and boards, DH, March 2011.
National Forum for People with Learning Difficulties **www.nationalforum.co.uk**
Learning Disabilities Observatory **www.improvinghealthandlives.org.uk**

Prison healthcare

People in prison have generally poorer health than the population at large: 71 per cent have two or more mental health disorders, and 70 per cent have a concurrent drug and/or alcohol problem; 10 per cent suffer from psychosis, while 80 per cent smoke. The ideal is to provide prisoners with access to the same quality and range of healthcare services as the public receives from the NHS. Schemes to tackle smoking and drug misuse and vaccinate against hepatitis B are common. Prisons have also implemented a care-planning system for prisoners at risk of suicide.

The DH and Ministry of Justice jointly operate an offender health division, responsible for leading a cross-government health and criminal justice programme. Its aim is improving health and social care outcomes for adults and children in contact with the criminal justice system, focusing on early intervention, liaison and diversion. Local liaison and diversion services at police stations and courts now intervene at an early stage to identify and assess those with mental health or substance misuse problems and help them into treatment. A national network of 101 local services has been established following the Government's pledge to make liaison and diversion services available nationally by 2014. The NHS Commissioning Board (see page 18) is to be responsible for commissioning prison healthcare.

Defence Medical Services

The Defence Medical Services (DMS) comprise the Headquarters Surgeon General, Joint Medical Command, Defence Dental Services and the medical organisations of the army, Royal Navy and Royal Air Force. The DMS are headed by the surgeon general, and over 7,000 regular uniformed medical personnel from all three services belong to them, working alongside the Ministry of Defence's civilian medical and dental staff. The DMS provide healthcare to 196,000 servicemen and women and 258,000 people in total, including in some circumstances family dependants of service personnel and entitled civilians.

The DMS run the Royal Centre for Defence Medicine in Birmingham and five other Ministry of Defence hospital units based in the NHS, 15 rehabilitation units across the UK and Germany and 15 departments of community mental health. They also provide some aspects of healthcare to other countries' personnel overseas, in both permanent military bases and areas of conflict. The DMS interact with the NHS at many levels: for example, their healthcare professionals train in the NHS, while 1,600 NHS staff belong to the British Reserve Forces. A partnership of eight NHS trusts provides inpatient mental healthcare to serving personnel across the UK under contract to the Ministry of Defence (MoD).

The NHS and MoD launched six community mental health pilot sites (including one in Scotland) in 2007, designed to make available within the NHS expert assessment and treatment for veterans with mental health problems.

Since 2008 all military veterans have been entitled to priority access to NHS secondary care for any conditions likely to be related to their service. There are about 5 million veterans in England. They are most likely to make use of audiology, mental health and orthopaedic services.

Personnel who are seriously injured receive a comprehensive assessment of their long-term needs before they leave the armed forces and then a regular review of their needs by an NHS case manager.

Further information

Briefing 210: Improving mental health services for veterans, Mental Health Network/NHS Confederation, November 2010.
An evaluation of six community mental health pilots for veterans of the armed forces, University of Sheffield, December 2010.
www.mod.uk/DefenceInternet/microsite/dms

Healthcare for asylum seekers and refugees

People with an outstanding application for refuge in the UK are entitled to use NHS services without charge. Although the High Court ruled in 2008 that failed asylum seekers may still be deemed 'ordinarily resident' in the UK and so also entitled to free NHS treatment, this judgement was overturned by the Court of Appeal in 2009. The DH has since decided that failed asylum seekers who cannot return home should be exempt from charges, as should children who arrive in the UK unaccompanied.

Asylum seekers are often from very different cultures, may not understand the principles behind the NHS, may not speak English and may have complex healthcare requirements.

The DH's Asylum Seeker and Migration Team coordinates healthcare policy for asylum seekers and refugees. It works across the DH and other government departments, and with health workers and service planners in the field. In particular, it liaises with the Home Office to try to ensure health and social care needs are met during the asylum process and taken into account in policy planning.

Asylum seekers usually stay in a network of induction centres on their arrival. Here they undergo an initial health assessment, normally by a nurse with access to a GP. Each asylum seeker is issued with a national hand-held health record.

The best model of healthcare for asylum seekers is integration into existing mainstream services. Where this is not possible immediately, the NHS locally may have to consider dedicated initiatives appropriate for asylum seekers new to an area.

Further information

Access to the NHS by foreign nationals – Government response to the consultation, DH, March 2011.

04 Policy and strategy: creating a 'vision' for the NHS

Making and implementing policy is a key strand of the Department of Health's work, and during a government's term of office it will publish a plethora of major policy documents designed to improve health and social care, turning political vision into action.

Policy and strategy are aimed both at the long term – for example, setting out a 'vision' of how the NHS might look in five or ten years' time – the medium term, such as the three-year cycle of the NHS's operational plans, and the short-term, such as the annual operating framework. And apart from initiatives specific to the health and social care system, the NHS is influenced by cross-government policy and strategy frameworks such as the spending review and structural reform plans.

The planning framework

The Government set its long-term strategy for public services in the 2010 spending review. It also decided the financial settlement for every government department and published structural reform plans that contain its priority outcomes for the spending review period. In turn, the DH published its priorities in its business plan, while the NHS operating framework outlines priorities for the health service over a three-year planning cycle.

Spending reviews

Every government carries out a long-term and fundamental review of all its expenditure soon after coming to power. The spending review is a Treasury-led process to allocate resources across all departments, according to the Government's priorities. Spending reviews set firm and fixed budgets over several years for each department. It is then up to departments to decide how best to manage and distribute this spending within their areas of responsibility. Before spending reviews were introduced in the 1990s, departmental budgets were set on a year-by-year basis, making multi-year planning more difficult.

The previous Labour Government held comprehensive spending reviews in 1998 and 2007. Following the coalition Government's first Budget in June 2010, setting out the overall level of public spending until 2014/15, it announced details of its spending review in October 2010, fixing budgets for each government department for the four years to 2014/15. The NHS settlement is contained within the DH's budget.

Key text: *Liberating the NHS*

Two months after the coalition Government came to power it published its first health white paper, *Equity and excellence: liberating the NHS*, together with a suite of complementary documents. The white paper outlined the far-reaching structural reorganisation now underway (see chapter 1), reinforced the importance of the market in the NHS in England and announced that the DH's role would be reduced. On its launch, *Liberating the NHS* was greeted as representing potentially the most significant change in the NHS's history. It contained the promise: 'In the next five years, the coalition Government will not produce another long-term plan for the NHS'.

Principles underlying the white paper include:
- the Government is committed to an NHS available to all, free at the point of use and based on need, not ability to pay
- health spending will increase in real terms annually for five years
- the Government's vision for the NHS is rooted in the coalition's 'core beliefs of freedom, fairness and responsibility'
- while the Government will be clear about *what* the NHS should do, it will not stipulate *how* to do it
- funding must be used efficiently: 'the single greatest priority for the next Parliament will be to reduce the deficit'.

It aimed to empower clinicians while rendering the NHS free from frequent and arbitrary political interference. Such was the scale of public and professional disquiet about the white paper that the Government held a 'listening exercise' led by the NHS Future Forum (see page 108) to consult on the changes as the Health and Social Care Bill was passing through Parliament. After some adjustment, the bill resumed its passage and has since become the Health and Social Care Act 2012.

Further information
Equity and excellence: liberating the NHS, DH, July 2010.
Liberating the NHS: legislative framework and next steps, DH, December 2010.

Key organisation: NHS Future Forum

By early 2011, concern among the public, healthcare professionals and MPs about the Government's plans for reorganising the NHS led ministers to resume consultation on the proposals while the bill intended to make them law was still being considered by Parliament. The Secretary of State announced that the Government was 'to take advantage of a natural break in the legislative process to pause, listen and reflect'.

The NHS Future Forum, a group of 45 senior professionals from health and social care, was set up to carry out an intensive eight-week 'listening exercise' during April and May. Its brief was to act as an independent advisory panel noting people's concerns, reporting on what was heard and offering advice to the Prime Minister, Deputy Prime Minister and Secretary of State on how the plans might be improved.

Its four core themes were:
- choice and competition
- public accountability and patient involvement
- clinical advice and leadership
- education and training.

Forum members attended 250 events and heard opinions from over 8,000 people, including 250 organisations. The Government accepted its recommendations and altered the Health and Social Care Bill accordingly. The Government then asked the Forum to continue its conversations with patients, service users and professionals to provide independent advice on how to:
- make information improve health, care and wellbeing
- develop the healthcare workforce
- ensure the reorganisation leads to better integration of services
- ensure the public's health remains at the heart of the NHS.

For this, the Forum held more than 300 events, which attracted 12,000 people. Once again, the Government accepted its recommendations. The Forum also influenced the 2012/13 NHS operating framework (see page 110).

Further information

Summary report on proposed changes to the NHS, NHS Future Forum, June 2011.
Government response to the NHS Future Forum report, DH, June 2011.
Summary report – second phase, NHS Future Forum, January 2012.

The scale of the deficit provided the main context for the 2010 spending review, prompting the Government to take radical action to limit public expenditure. However, to honour its commitment to protect health spending, the NHS budget is planned to increase by 0.4 per cent in real terms to 2014/15 (see page 168). The Chancellor's Autumn Statement in 2011 implied that the NHS would not see higher spending for a long time, with current funding levels set to persist into the next Parliament.

Further information
Spending review 2010, HM Treasury, October 2010.
Autumn Statement 2011, HM Treasury, November 2011.

Structural reform plans

Until the 2010 general election, the DH's medium-term objectives were defined by its public service agreement (PSA) made with the Treasury. The coalition Government abolished PSAs, replacing them with structural reform plans (SRPs). The DH's SRP is included in its business plan for 2011–15. Its five main priorities are to:
• integrate health and care systems around the needs of patients and users
• promote better health outcomes
• revolutionise NHS accountability
• promote public health
• reform social care.

The DH also agreed four 'major responsibilities' to:
• maintain performance on waiting times
• run an efficient and effective department of state
• help prepare for emergencies
• devolve leadership of information technology development.

A monthly report on progress in meeting the SRP commitments appears on the DH website.

Further information
Business plan 2011–2015, DH, July 2011.
Department of Health annual report and accounts 2010–11, TSO, September 2011.
www.dh.gov.uk

NHS operating framework

The annual operating framework sets out the business and planning arrangements for the NHS for the coming year. The framework for 2012/13 describes the national priorities and system levers the NHS needs in order to change services while maintaining and improving quality and finance. It assigns four 'key themes' for all NHS organisations during the year:
- putting patients at the centre of decision-making
- completing the last year of transition to the new system
- increasing the pace of the quality, innovation, productivity and prevention (QIPP) challenge (see page 170)
- maintaining and improving performance, including ensuring the NHS Constitution right to treatment within 18 weeks is met.

Key areas for improvement are dementia and care of older people, carers support and military and veteran health. Allocations to primary care trusts will grow by at least 2.5 per cent in 2012/13, while the running cost of clinical commissioning groups will be £25 per head of population.

Further information

The operating framework for the NHS in England 2012/13, DH, November 2011.
Briefing 232: Operating framework for the NHS in England 2012/13, NHS Confederation, December 2011.

Equality and diversity

Eliminating discrimination and disadvantage in the healthcare workforce and reducing health inequalities in the population are major policy aims of the DH and the NHS. Like all other public bodies, both have a legal duty to eliminate discrimination, harassment and victimisation, advance equality of opportunity and promote good community relations.

Equality Act 2010

The Equality Act 2010 outlaws discrimination on grounds of:
- age
- disability
- gender reassignment
- marriage and civil partnership
- pregnancy and maternity
- race
- religion or belief
- sex
- sexual orientation.

The Act includes a new public sector equality duty, which demands equality issues be taken into account when developing policy. DH officials must analyse all available evidence to establish whether their policies or practices meet the aims of the public sector equality duty. Boards of NHS organisations are required to explicitly provide assurance, and disclose any non-compliance with equality legislation, through their annual statement on internal control.

The DH's equality and human rights assurance group has set up a two-year transformation programme to develop a long-term cultural shift in the health and adult social care system with the aim of embedding equalities across policies, programmes and service delivery.

Further information
Briefing 74: The Equality Act 2010: employment implications for the NHS, NHS Employers, October 2010.

NHS Equality and Diversity Council
The NHS Equality and Diversity Council (EDC), set up in 2009, has a strategic role to help the NHS comply with the Equality Act 2010, ensuring services and workplaces are fair and diverse, with equality of opportunity and treatment for all. Its vision is: 'a personal, fair and diverse health and care service that draws the best from its communities and understands, respects and caters for all using and working within it'. Its aims are that:
• services focus on improvements in health outcomes and experiences, for all their community
• services are held to account by their communities for responding to the differing needs of all within them
• talent flourishes, free of discrimination with everyone having fair opportunities to progress
• all staff feel their contributions are recognised and that they count as part of their organisations
• services are demonstrably compliant with statutory duties, in letter and spirit, striving to go beyond these.

Membership includes representatives from the NHS, DH, trade unions, patient groups, regulators and voluntary sector.

Key text: NHS Constitution

'The NHS belongs to the people...' The NHS Constitution, which applies only to the health service in England, comprises:

- seven key principles that govern how the NHS operates, such as providing a comprehensive service and value for money
- rights and pledges to patients and the public about matters such as access, quality, respect, choice and complaints
- responsibilities that patients and public owe the NHS, such as keeping appointments and treating staff with respect
- staff rights concerning issues such as working environment, fair pay, representation and equal treatment
- staff responsibilities, including patient confidentiality and professional accountability
- six values, including respect and dignity, commitment to quality and compassion.

The Constitution attempts a balance between the need for clarity and avoiding litigation, between enshrining enduring values and principles while ensuring the NHS has flexibility to change. The Health Act 2009 placed a duty on all NHS organisations, private and third sector providers in England to take account of the Constitution. By law the Government must renew the Constitution every ten years, so that changes cannot take place without debate.

In its *Liberating the NHS* white paper (see page 107) the coalition Government pledged: 'We will uphold the NHS Constitution', although it has introduced several changes:

- NHS staff are expected to raise concerns about safety, malpractice or wrongdoing at work that may affect patients, public, other staff or the organisation as soon as possible
- the NHS will support all staff who raise such concerns, responding to and investigating concerns
- highlighting the Constitution's existing legal right for staff to raise such concerns without suffering any detriment.

Staff with concerns about patient care can call a free whistle-blowing helpline on 08000 724 725 weekdays between 8am and 6pm, with an out-of-hours answering service.

Further information

The NHS Constitution for England, NHS, March 2012.

The handbook to the NHS Constitution for England, DH, March 2012.

The NHS Constitution and whistleblowing – consultation report: September 2011, DH, October 2011.

Equality Delivery System

The EDC initiated the NHS Equality Delivery System. Launched in 2011, its purpose is to help the NHS deliver personal, fair and more diverse health services, and ensure staff from all backgrounds can thrive and develop. EDS is a framework tool that will enable NHS organisations to:

- prioritise better access to screening and other services for disabled people
- provide better primary care experiences for people from black and minority ethnic backgrounds
- ensure everyone, no matter what their sexual orientation or religious beliefs, can talk in confidence to clinicians about their identity
- make adjustments in the workplace for staff who need support in caring for younger and older dependants.

EDS supports NHS organisations in meeting various equality requirements, including those of the public sector equality duty, the NHS Constitution and the NHS outcomes framework (see page 126).

05 Quality and safety

The NHS is committed to providing high-quality care, which means continually striving to improve clinical standards and patient experience, using resources efficiently and ensuring patients' safety. Quality and safety criteria are set and monitored nationally, with every organisation's performance assessed and made public. Concerns about healthcare-acquired infections and variations in outcomes have brought renewed emphasis on patient safety and effectiveness.

Ensuring quality

The Government's NHS reorganisation is intended to produce a health service that achieves quality and outcomes that are among the world's best, and which refuses to tolerate unsafe and substandard care. It wants the NHS to be more transparent, with more accountability for quality and results.

Improving quality was a constant refrain throughout the previous Labour Government's health policy too, from the 1997 white paper that promised the service 'will have quality at its heart', to the then health minister Lord Darzi's 2008 Next Stage Review, which emphasised 'quality as the organising principle' of the NHS, 'at the heart of all that we do'. The review insisted that quality be understood from the patient's perspective, and defined it as comprising:
• patient safety
• patient experience
• effectiveness of care.

The coalition Government's *Liberating the NHS* white paper said: 'We recognise the importance of Lord Darzi's work, in putting a stronger emphasis on quality', while the National Quality Board (see opposite) noted in 2011: 'The NHS has coalesced around the definition of quality set out by Lord Darzi'. As a result, *Liberating the NHS* promised 'increasing amounts of robust information', comparable between providers, on safety, experience and effectiveness.

NHS organisations have a statutory duty to ensure the quality of their services, just as they have always had to keep their organisations financially solvent. Indeed, by law they now have to publish 'quality accounts' (see page 121). Other measures designed to foster quality include CQUIN (see page 122), adjustments to the tariff system to link increases in payments to specific quality goals (see page 162) and registration with the Care Quality Commission (see page 151). In addition, the Government plans to expand use of patient-reported outcome measures (see page 126), NICE quality standards (see page 123), national

The NQB is intended to provide strategic oversight and leadership in quality across the NHS. Members include the NHS medical director, chief medical and nursing officers and the chairs of the Care Quality Commission, NICE and Monitor, as well as leaders from the charity and third sectors, academe, social care and the Royal Colleges.

The board's role is 'to champion quality and ensure alignment in quality throughout the NHS'. It oversees work to improve quality indicators and advises the Secretary of State. For example, the NQB suggested practical steps to safeguard quality during the NHS reorganisation.

Further information

Maintaining and improving quality during the transition: safety, effectiveness, experience – part one 2011–12, NQB, March 2011.

clinical audit and patient surveys. Instead of using targets to measure NHS organisations' performance, they will be judged on the outcomes they achieve (see page 126).

Further information

High quality care for all: NHS Next Stage Review final report, DH, July 2008.
Liberating the NHS: an information revolution, DH, October 2010.

Quality governance

After several serious failures of quality in the 1990s – such as the murders committed by Dr Harold Shipman and the problems in Bristol Royal Infirmary's paediatric cardiology service – the concept of clinical governance emerged. Since it was first articulated in 1998, clinical governance has become widely accepted in the NHS, bringing together the culture, structures and processes that organisations, clinical teams and individual clinicians need to assure and improve care quality.

Clinical governance was traditionally the realm of clinicians and clinical managers within NHS trusts. But while frontline clinical teams are responsible for delivering quality care, each organisation's board is responsible for creating a culture that enables clinicians to work at their best. It must have in place arrangements for measuring and monitoring quality and for raising issues at board level where necessary. Clinical governance is therefore only part of a broader concept – quality governance.

A board's responsibilities for quality are to ensure:
- the essential standards of quality and safety (as determined by the Care Quality Commission's registration requirements – see page 151) are at a minimum being met by every service
- the organisation is striving for continuous quality improvement in every service
- every staff member who has contact with patients, or whose actions directly impact on patient care, is motivated and enabled to deliver effective, safe and person-centred care.

Boards should encourage a culture where services are improved by learning from mistakes: staff, patients and their families should be encouraged to identify areas for improvement and not be afraid to speak out.

Monitor (see page 148) defines quality governance as 'the combination of structures and processes at and below board level to lead on trust-wide quality performance'. It includes:
- ensuring required standards are achieved
- investigating and taking action on sub-standard performance
- planning and driving continuous improvement
- identifying, sharing and ensuring delivery of best practice
- identifying and managing risks to quality of care.

Quality governance involves formulating a strategy; ensuring the organisation has the requisite capabilities; fostering an appropriate culture; putting in place the necessary processes and structures and measuring outcomes. Quality governance arrangements should complement, and be fully integrated with, the governance arrangements for other board responsibilities, such as finance governance and research governance.

Further information

Quality governance in the NHS – a guide for provider boards, NQB, March 2011.

Clinical audit

Clinical audit is an important instrument of quality governance, providing rich data to support service improvement, better information for patients and revalidation of clinicians. It 'aims to assess the extent to which care is consistent with best practice and/or achieves expected outcomes'. With education and research it is one of the medical profession's three core responsibilities, but unlike them has lacked a national strategy and coherent programme – despite participation being mandatory for all doctors since 1989.

The National Advisory Group on Clinical Audit and Enquiries (NAGCAE) – previously known as the National Clinical Audit Advisory Group, since it was set up in 2006 – is a 'wide and inclusive' forum to enhance the existing programme of national clinical audits and support NHS staff involved in audits in their own organisations. It also seeks to improve connections between national clinical audits regardless of how they are funded, between audit and IT, revalidation and research and development.

NAGCAE also acts as the steering group for the National Clinical Audit and Patients' Outcomes Programme (NCAPOP), which commissions national audits, consults those with an interest in audit and develops resources for them. NCAPOP is administered by the Healthcare Quality Improvement Partnership (HQIP), a consortium of the Royal College of Nursing, Academy of Medical Royal Colleges and National Voices.

The *Liberating the NHS* white paper said: 'The role of clinical audit in comparing the effectiveness of different clinical approaches and in identifying areas for quality improvement is critical and we expect to see participation in clinical audit as a professional norm.' The Government also wants clinical audit data made widely available and used to inform quality accounts.

Data on all deaths that take place in NHS hospitals and within 30 days of discharge was published for the first time in 2011. The summary hospital-level mortality indicator (SHMI) compares the actual number of patients who die following treatment at a trust with the number who would be expected to die, given the characteristics of the patients treated there. The SHMI shows mortality rates for every acute non-specialist trust in England, providing a single comprehensive indicator that will be used consistently across the NHS.

Waiting times are an important factor in patients' perception and experience of care. The NHS Constitution gives patients the right to access services within maximum waiting times, including the right to start consultant-led treatment within a maximum of 18 weeks from referral for non-urgent conditions. If this is not possible, the Constitution requires the NHS to take reasonable steps to offer patients suitable alternative providers.

The right does not apply if the patient chooses to wait longer, or if delaying treatment is in their best clinical interests – for example, where stopping smoking or losing weight are likely to improve the treatment outcome. Neither does the right apply where it is clinically appropriate for the condition to be actively monitored in secondary care without clinical intervention or diagnostic procedures, or if the patient fails to attend appointments.

NHS organisations must achieve the 18-week standard for 90 per cent of admitted patients and 95 per cent of patients who do not need to be admitted to hospital.

The Government expects less than 1 per cent of patients to wait longer than six weeks for a diagnostic test. The NHS Constitution also gives patients the right to be seen by a cancer specialist within a maximum of two weeks from GP referral for urgent referrals where cancer is suspected.

Each trust has a single SHMI value categorised as 'as expected', 'higher than expected' and 'lower than expected' mortality rates. The data shows most trusts' rates fall within an expected range.

Hospital mortality ratios are complex indicators that have prompted international debate about their definition and interpretation. The DH acknowledges the indicator is still 'experimental' and refinements will have to be made in the future.

Further information
What is clinical audit?, DH, October 2009.
Liberating the NHS: an information revolution, DH, October 2010.
Briefing 208: Hospital standardised mortality rations: their uses and abuses, NHS Confederation, October 2010.
Healthcare Quality Improvement Partnership **www.hqip.org.uk**

National service frameworks

National service frameworks (NSFs) or strategies are evidence-based programmes setting quality standards and specifying services that should be available for a particular condition or care group across the whole NHS. They are intended to eradicate local variations in standards and services, raise standards generally, promote collaboration between organisations and contribute to improving public health. Each identifies key interventions, puts in place a strategy to support implementation and establishes an agreed timescale.

Each NSF was developed with assistance from an external reference group of health professionals, service users and carers, health service managers, partner agencies and other advocates. The DH supported the groups and managed the overall process. They cover:
- cancer
- child health and maternity
- coronary heart disease
- chronic obstructive pulmonary disease
- diabetes
- kidney disease
- long-term conditions
- mental health
- older people
- stroke.

Quality accounts

Under the Health Act 2009 all providers of NHS care must publish annual 'quality accounts' indicating the quality of the care they provide, just as they publish financial accounts. Quality accounts require boards to consider the quality of their services, their priorities for improvement and how they intend to achieve them. They are not intended to be a comprehensive assessment of every service, nor to supply patients with information they need to make an informed choice about services, although they are published on the NHS Choices website (see page 205). Acute and mental health trusts must have their quality accounts externally audited.

The *Liberating the NHS* white paper said: 'We want quality accounts to evolve over time and, like financial accounts, become more standardised as organisations gain experience in this type of reporting'. The National Quality Board has recommended all trusts report on a small number of mandatory indicators aligned with the NHS outcomes framework (see page 126), while the DH is exploring the feasibility of extending this requirement to independent sector providers of NHS-funded services from 2014/15.

CQUIN

The Commissioning for Quality and Innovation (CQUIN) payment framework makes part of a provider's income conditional on quality and innovation. It is intended to ensure contracts include quality improvement plans by allowing commissioners to link a specific proportion of providers' contract income to achieving locally agreed goals. For example, if a commissioner has concerns about stroke services, the provider could undertake to increase the percentage of stroke patients with access to scanning within three hours of admission – a process known to improve outcomes – to an agreed level.

In 2012/13, the amount that can be earned under CQUIN has increased to 2.5 per cent of contract income. All CQUIN schemes are required to include four national goals:
• reduce avoidable death, disability and chronic ill health from venous-thromboembolism
• improve responsiveness to personal needs of patients
• improve diagnosis of dementia in hospitals
• use the 'NHS safety thermometer'.

Further information
Using the commissioning for quality and innovation (CQUIN) payment framework, DH, December 2008.
The operating framework for the NHS in England 2012/13, DH, November 2011.

Quality and outcomes framework
The QOF is a voluntary incentive scheme to encourage high-quality services in general practice, and was introduced as part of the general medical services contract in 2004. It sets out a range of national standards based on the best available research evidence. The standards are divided into four domains:
• clinical standards linked to the care of patients suffering from chronic disease

- organisational standards relating to records and information, communicating with patients, education and training, medicines management and clinical and practice management
- additional services, covering cervical screening, child health surveillance, maternity services and contraceptive services
- patient experience, including assessing access to GP appointments measured by the GP patient survey.

A set of indicators – reviewed annually by NICE – has been developed for each domain to describe different aspects of performance. Practices are free to choose the domains they want to focus on and the quality standards to which they aspire. They receive payments against the indicators, which are adjusted according to list size and prevalence of disease. About 15 per cent of practice payments nationally are made through QOF.

NICE quality standards

NICE (see page 148) is developing a library of 150 quality standards – expected to be complete by July 2015 – to clarify the clinical evidence and guidance available to clinicians, commissioners and patients. They will be a 'final distillation' of clinical best practice, derived from the best available evidence from NICE guidance and other sources accredited by NHS Evidence (see page 191) to provide a set of specific, concise quality statements and associated measures. Produced in collaboration with health and social care professionals, each makes clear what quality care looks like to help end variations in care quality: they are reflected in the commissioning outcomes framework and in payment and incentive mechanisms such as QOF and CQUIN (see opposite). The Government intends the standards will be central to improving outcomes, acting as the bridge between the outcomes the NHS seeks to attain and the processes and structures necessary to do so. From 2012 they are also being developed for social care.

Further information

Healthcare quality standards – process guide, NICE, January 2012.

eradicating mixed-sex accommodation

To protect patients' privacy and dignity, men and women ought not to have to share sleeping areas, bathrooms or toilets when admitted to hospital. Despite repeated initiatives, this has remained a stubborn problem in the NHS. Until recently, nearly a quarter of patients reported being in a mixed-sex sleeping area when first admitted to hospital.

In 2009 the NHS undertook a six-month intensive drive to 'all but eliminate' mixed-sex accommodation, backed by a £100 million 'privacy and dignity fund'. More than 1,157 projects were planned across 396 sites belonging to over 200 organisations. In addition to new and refurbished same-sex sanitary facilities such as bathrooms, work included erecting separating walls, providing same-sex lounges and improved partitions, as well as implementing approved bed-management systems.

Since April 2011 hospitals have been fined £250 a day for each patient placed in mixed-sex accommodation. By December 2011, cases had fallen from 11,800 (out of 1.4 million patients) a year earlier to 767, with 73 per cent of trusts reporting no cases.

Indicators for Quality Improvement

NHS clinical teams have access via the Information Centre's website to more than 200 indicators generally accepted as effective measures of high-quality care. They can use these to assess local quality improvement. The Indicators for Quality Improvement have been selected with the Royal Colleges, and they cover ten care pathways using the three key dimensions of quality – safety, effectiveness and patient experience. Coverage will be expanded over the next few years, and most data will eventually appear on the NHS Choices website. The long-term aim is to build an extensive menu of indicators to help all the NHS understand and improve the quality of services.

www.ic.nhs.uk/mqi

Patient surveys

Listening to patients' views is essential for a patient-centred health service. To deliver improvements, the NHS has to know what people need and expect from it, and how well they think the service has responded to their needs and expectations. The programme of national patient surveys has three aims:

• to provide feedback for local quality improvement

- to assess users' experience for performance ratings, inspections and reviews
- to monitor patients' experience nationally.

The NHS national patient survey programme is the longest established, and one of the largest, patient survey programmes in the world: since 2002, several million patients have taken part in surveys. The Care Quality Commission (see page 147) is now responsible for carrying out national survey programmes on a rolling basis. Surveys have included adult inpatients and outpatients in acute hospitals, maternity services and community mental health services. For example, in 2011 over 17,000 patients from 65 mental health trusts took part, and 59 per cent rated their care excellent or very good.

The DH launched a GP patient survey in 2006. It is sent twice a year to 5 million patients of GP practices throughout England. It asks about aspects of accessing care – from making an appointment and experience of reception through to the clinical consultation – as well as other services such as dentistry and out-of-hours provision.

Each trust is required to obtain feedback from its own patients about their experiences of care. These surveys are intended to:
- track changes in patients' experience at trusts, year on year
- provide information for local quality improvement initiatives
- inform each trust's performance ratings and the performance indicators.

Trusts can seek support in carrying out their surveys from the NHS survey co-ordination centre, run by Picker Institute Europe on behalf of the Care Quality Commission, which can also help patients who are taking part in surveys.

Patients may also rate the service they received in hospital or at a GP practice using the NHS Choices website (see page 205).

Further information
NHS survey co-ordination centre **www.nhssurveys.org**
GP Patient Survey **www.gp-patient.co.uk/surveyresults**

PROMs

Assessing effectiveness of care means understanding success rates from different treatments, including clinical measures such as mortality or survival rates and measures of clinical improvement. But the patient's perspective is just as important. Patient-reported outcome measures (PROMs) are a method for collecting information on the clinical quality of care as reported by patients themselves. Since 2009 all providers of hip replacements, knee replacements, groin hernia surgery and varicose vein surgery must invite patients undergoing one of these procedures – more than 200,000 a year – to complete a pre-operative PROMs questionnaire. Some months after their operation patients are sent a follow-up questionnaire. The comparable data on their quality of life is then used to calculate a numerical value for the improvement to their health. There are plans to extend PROMs into other areas and procedures.

Further information
Guidance on the routine collection of patient reported outcome measures (PROMs),
DH, December 2008.

Assessing performance: the NHS outcomes framework
The NHS outcomes framework aims to:
• provide an overview of how the NHS performs nationally
• act as a mechanism to hold the NHS Commissioning Board to account
• be a catalyst for quality improvement and outcome measurement
  throughout the NHS.

The framework contains 60 NHS performance indicators within
five 'domains':
• preventing people from dying prematurely
• enhancing quality of life for people with long-term conditions
• helping people recover from episodes of ill health or following injury
• ensuring people have a positive experience of care
• ensuring people are treated in a safe environment and protected from
  avoidable harm.

For 2012/13, individual indicators include reducing premature mortality from the four major causes of death: cardiovascular disease, respiratory disease, liver disease and cancer. They also include increasing one- and five-year survival rates after treatment for breast, lung and colorectal cancers. Reducing infant mortality, neonatal mortality and stillbirths are also included, as well as reducing the number of premature deaths in people with learning disabilities and those with serious mental illness. The NHS will also measure whether young people and children's experience of care has improved.

Further information
The NHS outcomes framework 2012/13, DH, December 2011.

Ensuring patient safety

The NHS's first priority is its patients' safety. No healthcare system can be entirely risk-free but it must do everything possible to minimise unintended harm, whether from healthcare-associated infections or medical accidents. Failure to do so rapidly undermines public confidence in the system.

Over 1 million patient safety incidents in the NHS are reported every year. Of these:
- 69 per cent result in no harm to the patient
- 24 per cent result in low harm
- 6 per cent result in moderate harm
- 0.6 per cent result in death or severe harm.

The Government intends to introduce an enforceable 'duty of candour' into contracts with all providers of NHS care. This would insist that providers were open and honest with patients or their families about mistakes, ensuring they were informed about any investigations. It is seen as a key component of developing a safety culture.

Further information
Implementing a 'duty of candour'; a new contractual requirement on providers – proposals for consultation, DH, October 2011.

Central Alerting System

The web-based Central Alerting System (CAS) distributes all patient safety alerts and related guidance to the NHS and other health and social care providers. These include emergency alerts, drug alerts, 'Dear Doctor' letters and medical device alerts issued on behalf of the Medicines and Healthcare Products Regulatory Agency and the DH. The public can access CAS, although part of the site is open only to registered NHS users.
www.cas.dh.gov.uk

Combating healthcare-associated infections

HCAIs are infections acquired in hospitals or as a result of healthcare interventions. They are caused by a wide variety of micro-organisms, often by bacteria that normally live harmlessly in or on the body. While HCAIs are most likely to be acquired during treatment in acute hospitals, like other bacterial infections they are fairly prevalent in the community and can occur in other care settings. They can have severe consequences for patients as well as costs for the NHS. An HCAI adds on average three to ten days to a patient's stay in hospital and costs between £4,000 and £10,000 to treat.

HCAIs are a worldwide problem. Since the mid-1980s, prevalence in hospitals worldwide has been 5 to 10 per cent; in England it had reached 8.2 per cent by 2004. For most patients, the risk of acquiring an infection is low, and lower still for those who spend only one or two days in hospital.

During the last 25 years the organisms themselves have changed, with new strains developing and others being controlled. The NHS faces particular problems with MRSA and C. difficile. MRSA can infect surgical wounds and ulcers, and if it enters the bloodstream cause chest infections. It is usually spread through skin-to-skin contact, or by touching materials and surfaces contaminated from someone infected with MRSA. Measures such as hand washing and using alcohol handrub can help reduce the spread, as can isolating infected patients.

Toxins released by C. difficile cause diarrhoea, which can be severe and life-threatening. In most cases, the infection develops after cross-infection from another patient. Over 80 per cent of cases occur in people aged over 65. Alcohol handrubs are ineffective for C. difficile. Isolation of infected patients coupled with thorough hand-washing before and after contact, use of gloves and aprons and cleaning the ward are usually successful in prevention and control.

A wide range of measures to tackle HCAIs have been instigated in recent years and are producing results. By the end of 2011, MRSA cases had fallen by 86 per cent since 2003/04, and C. difficile cases had fallen by 64 per cent since 2007/08, when enhanced surveillance began. In mid-2011, 25 acute trusts had had no MRSA infections for a year. In 2012/13 the NHS is being asked to reduce MRSA infections by a further 29 per cent and C. difficile by 17 per cent. This would bring annual numbers of MRSA infections down to 880 and reduce C. difficile infections from 19,754 to 16,100.

An HCAI technology programme has helped accelerate development and adoption of new technologies to help fight infection. As part of a Design Bugs Out project, a partnership between the DH and the Design Council, designers were challenged to devise new furniture, equipment and services for hospital wards to enhance cleanliness. Four new bedside furniture designs, trialled in eight hospitals, were made available at the end of 2011. This was the first time for many years that hospital furniture design had been assessed and evaluated.

Further information

Design bugs out – product evaluation report: the healthcare associated infection technology innovation programme, DH, November 2011.

http://hcai.dh.gov.uk

Spotlight on policy: 'never events'

'Never events' are serious and largely preventable patient safety incidents that can cut life short or result in serious impairment. They should never be allowed to happen in a high-quality service. A list was first drawn up for the NHS in 2009 covering eight never events, including wrong-site surgery, instruments left inside the patient after surgery, inpatient suicide while on one-to-one observation, in-hospital maternal death from post-partum haemorrhage after elective caesarean and transferred prisoners absconding from medium or high-secure mental health services.

The list has now been extended to 25 and includes severe scalding, transfusing the wrong type of blood and misidentifying patients by failing to use the standard wristband.

Payment from commissioners will be withheld where never events occur. In the year to June 2010, 111 never events took place, costing the NHS £3.9 million.

Further information

The 'never events' list 2012/13, DH, January 2012.

06 Accountability and regulation

NHS organisations must demonstrate strategic and operational accountability: they must have a clear and well-evidenced long-term plan, and show transparency in their day-to-day decisions. They are accountable to local people who are consumers of their services and taxpayers who fund the NHS: therefore, they have a duty to maintain the highest standards of quality and safety, as well as to balance the books and provide value for money.

Clinical commissioning groups will be accountable outwards to their local communities and upwards to the NHS Commissioning Board, which in turn will be accountable through the Secretary of State to Parliament and the electorate. Foundation trusts are also accountable to their local communities, to Monitor and to Parliament.

The Government summarised the purpose of its NHS reorganisation: 'Our aim is to put patients, carers and local communities at the heart of the NHS, shifting decision-making as close as possible to individual patients and carers by devolving power to professionals and providers and liberating them from top-down control.'

NHS organisations are immediately accountable to independently appointed boards, and they have a duty to involve and consult patients and the public. They can also be called to account by their local authority, through the health and wellbeing board and the health overview and scrutiny committee. They must also answer to a variety of national regulators and inspectorates. The healthcare professions too are subject to their own regulatory bodies, which set standards and police them.

The role of boards and governing bodies

Duties and responsibilities

In NHS provider organisations, boards take corporate responsibility for strategies and actions. With current policy emphasis on decentralisation, local leadership and autonomy, their role is more important than ever.

Boards consist of executives (including the chief executive and finance director) and non-executives plus a chair. The chair and non-executives are lay people drawn from the local community.

A board's role is:
- formulating the organisation's strategy
- holding the organisation to account for achieving the strategy and ensuring that systems of control are robust and reliable
- shaping a positive culture for the board and the organisation.

An effective board:
- is informed by the external context in which it operates
- is informed by and shapes information about the organisation's performance
- builds a healthy dialogue with patients, public and staff, and feels accountable to all of them.

Legally, there is no distinction between the board duties of executive and non-executive directors: they both share responsibility for the organisation's direction and control. The board is expected to bring about change by making best use of all its resources – financial, staffing, physical infrastructure and knowledge – and working with staff and partner organisations to meet the public's and patients' expectations. As leaders, board members are expected to understand opportunities for improving services and motivate others to bring them about.

Boards make plans to achieve the Government's objectives for healthcare, guided by long-term strategy and shorter-term aims such as the NHS's operating framework. Boards have increasing scope to pace their plans to reflect local circumstances, and have a large say over how to achieve them – in theory at least. All boards sign off an annual business plan setting out the year's objectives, and it is the whole board's function to ensure progress.

NHS boards are obliged to ensure their organisations have an ethos and culture of public service that reflects and respects public expectation. The need for public accountability means boards must conduct business in an open and transparent way that commands public confidence. Their meetings are usually open to the public, and should be understandable to the public.

Further information
The healthy NHS board: principles for good governance, National Leadership Centre, February 2010.

The chair

The chair's role is to:

- ensure the board develops a vision, strategies and clear objectives to deliver organisational purpose
- hold the chief executive to account for achieving the strategy
- ensure board committees that support accountability are properly constituted
- provide visible leadership in developing a positive culture for the organisation, and ensure this is reflected and modelled in their own and the board's behaviour and decision-making
- lead and support a constructive dynamic within the board, enabling contributions from all directors
- provide a safe point of access to the board for whistle-blowers
- ensure all board members are well briefed on the organisation's external context
- ensure requirements for accurate, timely and clear information to the board directors (and for foundation trusts, governors) are clear
- play a key role as an ambassador and build strong partnerships with patients and public; for foundation trusts, members and governors; clinicians and staff; key institutional stakeholders and regulators.

In general, a strong correlation exists between the quality of the chair's and chief executive's leadership and the organisation's success. Where an organisation is not delivering, questions can legitimately be asked about the quality of the board leadership.

Non-executive directors

Non-executive directors should:

- bring independence, external skills and perspectives to strategy development
- hold executives to account for achieving the strategy
- offer purposeful, constructive scrutiny and challenge
- chair or participate as members of key committees that support accountability
- actively support and promote a positive culture for the organisation and reflect this in their own behaviour
- provide a safe point of access to the board for whistle-blowers
- satisfy themselves of the integrity of financial and quality intelligence
- ensure the board acts in the best interests of the public
- ensure a senior independent director is available to members (and in foundation trusts, governors) if there are unresolved concerns.

The chief executive

The chief executive is responsible for ensuring the board is empowered to govern the organisation and its objectives are accomplished through effective and properly controlled executive action. A chief executive's main responsibilities are:

- leading strategy development
- leading the organisation in achieving the strategy
- establishing effective performance management arrangements and controls
- acting as the organisation's accountable officer
- providing visible leadership in developing a positive culture for the organisation, and ensuring this is reflected in their own and the executive's behaviour and decision-making
- ensuring all board members are well briefed on the organisation's external context
- ensuring provision of accurate, timely and clear information to board directors (and in foundation trusts, governors)
- playing a key role as an ambassador and building strong partnerships with patients and public; for foundation trusts, members and governors; clinicians and staff; key institutional stakeholders and regulators.

Board committees

NHS boards may delegate some of their powers to formally constituted committees. Some are set up to advise the board on a permanent basis, such as the:

- audit committee
- remuneration and terms of service committee
- clinical governance committee
- risk management committee.

Foundation trust boards

Foundation trusts have distinctive governance arrangements. Staff, patients and local people are eligible to become 'members' of the trust. Membership entitles them to vote at elections for the board of governors and to stand for election to the board. According to Monitor, foundation trusts had recruited an estimated 2.03 million members by 2011/12: each had just under 14,000 members on average.

The board of governors includes those elected by the trust members and staff, as well as people appointed by local authorities. Representatives

elected by patients and the public must be in the majority, while at least three must be elected by staff. The board of governors' role is to advise the board of directors on its forward plans. It also has the power to remove the chief executive.

Each foundation trust has a board of directors made up of non-executives appointed by the governors and executive directors appointed by the non-executives. This board is responsible for managing the foundation trust, including its day-to-day operation and forward business plan.

Board of directors' meetings concern the trust's operational business, with board of governors' meetings focusing more on members' needs and ensuring local communities can contribute to decision-making. Since the Health and Social Care Act 2012, foundation trusts must hold their board meetings in public.

Further information
Governors in NHS foundation trusts: what the law says you have to do, Monitor, April 2010.
Survey of NHS foundation trust governors 2010/11, Monitor, July 2011.
Current practice in NHS foundation trust member recruitment and engagement, Monitor, July 2011.

CCGs' governing bodies
Every clinical commissioning group must have a governing body with decision-making powers. In addition to GPs and two other clinicians, the governing body will have to include at least two lay members – one with a lead role in championing patient and public involvement, the other with a lead role in overseeing key elements of governance such as audit, remuneration and managing conflicts of interest. One lay member will act as the CCG's chair or deputy chair. If deputy, the lay member would take the chair's role for discussions and decisions involving a conflict of interest for the chair.

CCGs' governing bodies are not intended to represent every group, but they will have to include at least one registered nurse and one doctor who is a secondary care specialist. These must have no conflict of interest relating to the CCG's responsibilities: for example, they cannot be employed by a local provider.

The governing body's non-GP members should provide an independent perspective, informed by their expertise and experience. They will be appointed for their professional knowledge and its value to the CCG's

The Freedom of Information Act 2000 requires every public authority to adopt a 'publication scheme' that specifies the types of information the authority publishes, the form it takes and whether it charges for the information. Each scheme must be approved by the Information Commissioner, an independent public official responsible for overseeing operation of the Act, who also has powers of enforcement.

Since 2005, NHS organisations must answer requests for information within the terms of the individual right of access given by the Act. This applies to all types of recorded information held by the organisation regardless of its date, although the Act specifies some exemptions – such as information where the patient is identifiable. Anyone making a request must be told whether the organisation holds the information and, if so, be supplied with it – generally within 20 working days. Organisations also have a duty to provide advice or help to anyone seeking information. Where a request for information is denied, it may be possible to appeal against the decision.

Further information

Freedom of Information publication scheme – guide to information, DH, August 2011. Information Commissioner **www.ico.gov.uk**

governance, rather than their familiarity with the local health system. They are expected to help ensure the CCG effectively involves a range of healthcare professionals in decision-making. Governing bodies must meet in public and publish their minutes.

Before intervening in a CCG's affairs, the NHS Commissioning Board must always demonstrate reasonable grounds. If the Board needs to dissolve a CCG in the event of significant failure, it must consult the group concerned, local authorities and others.

Engaging patients and the public

Engaging patients and the public in health services can be interpreted in different ways.
• Individual patients may be involved together with health professionals in making decisions about their own care.

- Organisations may seek direct feedback from patients about their experiences of using services: patient experience is one of the three measures of quality – along with safety and effectiveness – against which services are judged, and part of the payment-by-results tariff (see page 162) is linked to it.
- Users of a particular service may be involved as a group in advising how it might be improved.
- Members of the public may be involved in making strategic decisions about how or where services are to be provided and future priorities.

Empowering both individuals and communities to play a greater role in shaping health and social care services has become a central aim of policy: not only have people said they want more influence over these services, but it can help organisations provide better service if they understand what patients and the local community want and know about their experience of using services. It also strengthens accountability, and helps build a relationship of confidence and trust between the NHS and the people it serves.

Since 2000 the health service has had an explicit duty to ensure patients and the public have a real say in how services are planned and developed. Further legislation in 2006 and 2007 strengthened the duty to involve and consult service users or their representatives.

The NHS Constitution (see page 112) establishes as an underlying principle that the health service will involve individual patients and the wider community, and be accountable to the public, communities and patients. It includes specific rights for patients to be involved in discussions and decisions about their healthcare, in planning healthcare services and in decisions about proposed changes and how services are run. The NHS also pledges to provide the information needed to enable this to happen.

The Health and Social Care Act 2012 continues this process. The Government's *Liberating the NHS* white paper (see page 107) declared that the slogan 'no decision about me without me' should come to epitomise an NHS where patients are involved fully in their own care, with decisions made in partnership with clinicians rather than by clinicians alone. In the accompanying consultation paper, *Local democratic legitimacy in health*, the Government stated: 'We want local people to have a greater say in decisions that affect their health and care and have a clear route to influence the services they receive.'

Patient and public engagement (PPE) means discussing with patients and the public their ideas, the organisation's plans, patients' experiences, why services need to change, what people want from services and how to make best use of resources.

The NHS Commissioning Board will have a national director-level role with responsibility for PPE. Health and wellbeing boards (see page 22) will have a duty to involve users and the public, while CCGs must state in their annual commissioning plans how they intend to involve patients and the public in commissioning decisions. CCGs and the NHS Commissioning Board will have to involve the public in any changes that affect patient services, not just those with a 'significant' impact. The Board will assess how effectively CCGs have discharged their duty to involve patients and the public as part of their annual assessment.

Since 2000, every trust has had to obtain feedback from patients about their experiences of care. Many seek direct patient feedback, including 'real-time' feedback, to improve their understanding of people's experiences of care. A DH report reviewing lessons from the investigation into Mid Staffordshire NHS Foundation Trust (see page 142) emphasised that organisations should take note of early, 'soft' and informal information that reveals consistent concerns from patients and the public.

Further information
Mid Staffordshire NHS Foundation Trust: a review of lessons learnt for commissioners and performance managers following the Healthcare Commission investigation, Dr David Colin-Thomé, DH, April 2009.
Liberating the NHS: local democratic legitimacy in health, DH, July 2010.
Discussion paper 11: Patient and public engagement in the new commissioning system, NHS Confederation, October 2011.

HealthWatch
HealthWatch is designed to be the new 'consumer champion' for health and adult social care. It will exist in two distinct forms: local HealthWatch and at national level, HealthWatch England.

Local HealthWatch is evolving from the existing 150 local involvement networks (LINks), the main vehicles for involving patients and the public in the NHS since 2008. But local HealthWatch will have additional functions and powers to hold to account local services. The aim is to give citizens and communities a stronger voice to influence and challenge how health and social care services are provided within their locality. Each will be an independent organisation, able to employ its own staff and volunteers.

At local level, HealthWatch will:
- ensure patients' and carers' views influence commissioning, through a seat on the health and wellbeing board
- provide advocacy and support to patients making a complaint
- be accountable to and funded by local authorities
- feed intelligence to HealthWatch England, alerting it to concerns about specific providers.

Commissioners and providers will have a duty to pay due regard to findings from local HealthWatch organisations. Local HealthWatch membership must be representative of local people and different users of services, including carers. The role of local HealthWatch is being tested by 75 pathfinders.

HealthWatch England will be a national body that enables the collective views of NHS and social care users to influence national policy. It will be a statutory committee of the Care Quality Commission and funded through it, with a chair who is a CQC non-executive director. It will:
- provide leadership, advice and support to local HealthWatch
- provide advice to the Secretary of State, NHS Commissioning Board, Monitor and the English local authorities – to which they must pay regard
- propose CQC investigations of poor services.

HealthWatch England will be launched in October 2012, and Local HealthWatch will be formally established in April 2013.

Further information
HealthWatch transition plan, DH, March 2011.
Local HealthWatch: a strong voice for people – the policy explained, DH, March 2012.

Patient advice and liaison services
Every trust should have a patient advice and liaison service (PALS) providing on-the-spot help and information about health services. PALS aim to:
- resolve concerns before they become major problems
- provide information to patients, carers and their families about local health services and put people in contact with local support groups
- tell people about the complaints procedure and independent complaints advocacy support

Spotlight on policy: human rights and healthcare

Human rights are based on the 'FREDA values' of fairness, respect, equality, dignity and autonomy. The Government has incorporated into UK law most of the rights defined in the European Convention through the Human Rights Act 1998. This was intended to bring about a culture of human rights in public services. Putting human rights at the heart of how health services are designed and delivered can improve experience and outcomes for patients and staff. It also supports aspirations for a personalised service.

The Act provides a framework that can help NHS organisations ensure individuals receive fair, dignified and equitable treatment. Of the 15 rights defined in the Act, most relevant to healthcare are the rights:
• not to be treated in an inhuman or degrading way
• to respect for private and family life, home and correspondence
• to liberty and the right to life
• not to be discriminated against.

Examples of human rights issues in practice include 'do not resuscitate' orders, unsanitary conditions, excessive force in restraint, staff disciplinary procedures, privacy on wards and family visits. NHS organisations can take a human rights-based approach by ensuring accountability and empowerment, by encouraging participation and involvement and by paying attention to vulnerable groups, ensuring they are not discriminated against.

Further information
Human rights in healthcare – a short introduction, DH, October 2008.

• act as an early-warning system by monitoring trends, highlighting gaps in service and making reports for action to trust managers.

The National PALS Network aims to promote PALS and support the professional development of PALS staff, as well as acting as a national voice for the service.

Further information
National PALS Network **www.pals.nhs.uk**

Kennedy Report

The inquiry into the deaths of child heart patients at Bristol Royal Infirmary between 1984 and 1995 was chaired by Professor Sir Ian Kennedy and made many important recommendations for change in the NHS, not least that there should be representation of patient interests on the inside of the NHS and at every level. The inquiry ran from 1998 to 2001, and its report was published in 2001.
www.bristol-inquiry.org.uk

Francis Report

A full public inquiry into failures in patient care at Mid Staffordshire NHS Foundation Trust between 2005 and 2009 is expected to report in mid-2012. Ordered by the Secretary of State and chaired by Robert Francis QC, it is examining why serious problems at the trust were not identified and acted on sooner. The inquiry will consider the role of commissioning, supervisory and regulatory organisations in relation to the trust.

An earlier independent inquiry led by Robert Francis QC made 18 recommendations, all of which the Government accepted when his report was published in February 2010. Among the shortcomings he found were:
• corporate focus on process at the expense of outcomes
• failure to listen to patients by properly considering their complaints
• staff disengaged from management
• insufficient attention to professional standards
• lack of support for staff through appraisal, supervision and professional development
• weak professional voice in management decisions
• some treatment of elderly patients tantamount to abuse of vulnerable people
• lack of external and internal transparency
• false reassurance taken from external assessments
• disregard for the significance of mortality statistics.

Key recommendations included:
• reviewing arrangements for the appointment, training, support and accountability of trust executive and non-executive directors
• setting up a working group to examine methodologies for compiling mortality statistics
• a further inquiry into why the commissioning, supervisory and regulatory bodies did not detect the trust's failings earlier.

Further information
Mid Staffordshire NHS Foundation Trust independent inquiry
www.midstaffsinquiry.com
Mid Staffordshire NHS Foundation Trust public inquiry
www.midstaffspublicinquiry.com

Complaints

Reforming complaints procedures

Since 2009, a single complaints system has existed for all health and local authority adult social care services in England. These unified arrangements aim to:

- resolve complaints locally in a more personal and flexible way
- ensure early and effective resolution and robust handling of all cases, not just the more complex
- make sure people with complaints have access to effective support, particularly those who find it difficult to make their views heard
- give people the option of going direct to the commissioner with a complaint about their GP, NHS dentist or pharmacist instead of complaining directly to the practice
- give people the option of going direct to their local authority where their care has been arranged by the local authority
- ensure organisations improve services by routinely learning from people's experiences.

The range of measures available locally to resolve complaints include:

- robust risk assessment to quickly deal with serious complaints, such as those involving abuse or unsafe practice
- a plan, agreed by the complainant, outlining how the complaint is going to be tackled, who will be involved and their roles, timescales and how the complainant will be kept informed of progress
- involvement of the most senior managers or clinicians at an early stage
- early face-to-face meetings between everyone concerned to make sure the circumstances giving rise to the complaint are clearly understood
- independent mediators when the relationship between the complainant and the NHS body has broken down
- people independent of the service provider, commissioning organisation or the locality to investigate where complaints cannot be resolved satisfactorily or complex issues are involved

- specialist advocates to help people with complex needs voice their complaint effectively and understand the organisation's response
- clear, effective leadership from the most senior managers to ensure complaints arrangements meet people's needs and services are improved.

Local organisations must make every effort to resolve the complaint, but if complainants are dissatisfied with the local response they may go directly to the Ombudsman.

In 2010/11, the NHS received 148,200 complaints, a 2.4 per cent decrease on the previous year.

The Ombudsman

The office of the Parliamentary and Health Service Ombudsman undertakes independent investigations into complaints about the NHS in England, as well as government departments and other public bodies. It is completely independent of the NHS and Government. In the NHS, the Ombudsman investigates complaints that a hardship or injustice has been caused by its failure to provide a service, by a failure in service or by maladministration. The Ombudsman looks into complaints against private health providers only if the treatment was funded by the NHS.

Complainants can only take their cases to the Ombudsman if they fail to achieve a resolution with the organisation or practitioner they are complaining against – for example, because of delays in dealing with a complaint locally or failure to get a satisfactory answer. The Ombudsman can consider complaints from a patient; a close member of the family, partner or representative, if the patient is unable to act for themselves; or from someone who has suffered injustice or hardship as a result of the actions of the NHS. A complaint will normally only be considered within a year of the events which gave rise to it, and only if the Ombudsman believes the NHS has not acted properly or has provided a poor service.

The Ombudsman publishes detailed reports of investigations, which identify common themes in complaints. The reports are intended to be used as training tools to improve services, and chief executives are asked to ensure all clinical directors and complaints managers are aware of them. They are also considered by the House of Commons public administration committee. www.ombudsman.org.uk

Independent Complaints Advocacy Services (ICAS)

ICAS are available across the country to help individuals pursue complaints about the NHS. Complainants can contact their local ICAS office direct, or through complaints managers at hospitals and GP practices, NHS Direct or the patient advice and liaison service. ICAS aims to ensure complainants have access to the support they need to articulate their concerns and navigate the complaints system. It can simply offer advice or write letters and attend meetings to speak on the complainant's behalf. In 2013/14, local authorities will take on responsibility for commissioning NHS complaints advocacy, and may if they wish commission local HealthWatch to provide them.

Reforming clinical negligence procedures

Although the NHS provides high-quality healthcare for millions of people every year, occasionally patients do not receive the treatment they should, or mistakes are made. In the UK and other developed countries, about 10 per cent of hospital admissions may result in some kind of adverse event, and a third of these patients will suffer severe illness or die. In NHS primary care, research suggests about 600 errors a day occur, mainly in diagnosis and treatment, of which a fifth will cause harm.

Anyone who suffers harm as a result of treatment must receive an apology, a clear explanation of what went wrong, proper treatment and care and, where appropriate, financial compensation. The NHS must ensure it learns from such experiences.

But legal proceedings for medical injury are slow, complex and costly. They divert clinical staff from providing care, and can damage morale as well as public confidence. The system encourages defensiveness and secrecy, which hampers the NHS from learning and improvement. The NHS Redress Act 2006 provided an alternative to litigation for less severe and less costly cases, aimed at shifting emphasis from attributing blame towards preventing harm, reducing risks and learning from mistakes, while avoiding the courts altogether. However, ministers decided against implementing the scheme in England and are exploring alternatives for settling less costly clinical negligence claims. The scheme is being implemented in Wales, while the Scottish Government is investigating the introduction of a no-fault compensation scheme.

Key organisation: **NHS Litigation Authority**

NHSLA, set up in 1995, handles negligence claims against NHS bodies in England, and operates a risk management programme to help raise standards and reduce incidents leading to claims. It also monitors human rights case law and coordinates equal-pay claims on the NHS's behalf.

In 2010/11 NHSLA received 8,655 claims for clinical negligence and paid out £863 million in damages and costs. At March 2011 it had 21,339 live claims. Fewer than 50 clinical negligence cases a year are contested in court, and 96 per cent of the NHSLA's cases are settled out of court. Claims are settled on average in a year and three months. Of all clinical claims handled since 2001:
- 38 per cent were abandoned by the claimant
- 45 per cent were settled out of court
- 3 per cent were settled in court
- 14 per cent are outstanding.

A review of the NHSLA praised its role and contribution but made recommendations for change, many of which the DH accepted.

Further information
Department of Health – NHS Litigation Authority industry review, Marsh, April 2011.
NHS Litigation Authority industry review: Department of Health response, January 2012.
www.nhsla.com

The number of clinical negligence claims against the NHS rose by 30 per cent in 2010/11, and cost £863 million (see above). Research suggests costs are being driven by the use of 'no win, no fee' lawyers, and often claimants' costs are disproportionate to the damages paid, particularly in low-value claims.

Further information
Complaints and litigation: sixth report of session 2010–12, House of Commons health committee, June 2011.

Regulation and inspection

NHS organisations and the healthcare professions are all subject to stringent regulation, audit and inspection to ensure they maintain high service standards and provide value for money.

The regulators

Many national bodies are responsible for regulating, auditing and inspecting various aspects of NHS services – some long-established, others more recent. Regulation covers numerous areas but is essentially a way of preventing conditions that may adversely affect patients' interests. It has helped mitigate against limited access to services, high prices, perverse incentives and lack of information, as well as ensuring safety and quality.

There are different regulators for Scotland (Healthcare Improvement Scotland, see page 213), Wales (Healthcare Inspectorate Wales, see page 227) and Northern Ireland (Regulation and Quality Improvement Authority, see page 235).

Further information

Liberating the NHS: regulating healthcare providers – a consultation on proposals, DH, July 2010.

The following are among the major national bodies regulating and inspecting the NHS.

Care Quality Commission

Operating since 2009, the CQC regulates the quality and safety of health and adult social care services, whether provided by the NHS, local authorities, private companies or voluntary organisations. Its functions are:
- registering health and adult social care providers to ensure they meet essential common safety and quality standards, and, with Monitor, developing a joint licensing process
- monitoring and inspecting all health and adult social care, including how the Mental Health Act is working
- using enforcement powers, such as fines, public warnings or closures, if standards are not met
- reporting the outcome of its work to the public and professionals.

Since 2010, health and adult social care providers must register with the CQC in order to provide services (see page 151). The CQC will host HealthWatch England (see page 139).

According to the National Audit Office, the CQC has had a difficult task in establishing itself and has not so far achieved value for money in regulating quality and safety.

Further information

Performance and capability review: Care Quality Commission, DH, February 2012.
The Care Quality Commission: regulating the quality and safety of health and adult social care, NAO, December 2011.
www.cqc.org.uk

Monitor

Established in 2004, Monitor's original function was authorising and regulating NHS foundation trusts. Under the NHS reorganisation it is to become the sector regulator for healthcare and, at a later date, for adult social care. Its role will be to promote economy, efficiency and effectiveness in the provision of services, protecting and promoting patients' interests – not, as was initially proposed, promoting competition as an end in itself. Until 2016 it will have a continuing role in assessing NHS trusts for foundation trust status, and for ensuring that foundation trusts are financially viable and well led.

With the CQC it will license providers of NHS services in England (see page 151), and:
• regulate prices – designing a pricing methodology and calculating the efficiency requirements for the sector, then using these to set prices in agreement with the NHS Commissioning Board
• enable integrated care and prevent anti-competitive behaviour – removing barriers to integration and tackling abuses and restrictions that act against patients' interests
• support service continuity – ensuring patients can continue to access care in the event of a provider failing.

Further information

The Health and Social Care Bill: Monitor's evolving role, Monitor, October 2011.
Protecting and promoting patients' interests: the role of sector regulation, DH, December 2011.
www.monitor-nhsft.gov.uk

National Institute for Health and Clinical Excellence (NICE)

NICE was set up in 1999 to reduce variation in the availability and quality of NHS treatments and care – the so-called 'postcode lottery'. Its evidence-based guidance helps resolve uncertainty about which medicines, treatments, procedures and devices represent the best quality care and which offer the best value for money. It also produces public health guidance, recommending best ways to encourage healthy living, promote wellbeing and prevent disease.

All its guidance and quality standards are developed by an independent committee of experts including clinicians, patients, carers and health economists. NICE's 30-strong citizens council provides it with advice that reflects the public's perspective on what are often challenging social and moral issues raised by NICE guidance. Under the NHS Constitution, patients have a right to treatments NICE has recommended.

The NHS outcomes framework (see page 126) is linked to NICE's quality standards (see page 123), while under the Health and Social Care Act, NICE's remit has been extended to produce quality standards for social care. Ministers expect that as value-based pricing of drugs is introduced (see page 169), NICE's role will evolve.
www.nice.org.uk

National Audit Office
Headed by the Comptroller and Auditor General, the NAO's role is to report direct to Parliament on how public bodies have spent central government money, conducting financial audits and assessing value for money. It works closely with the Commons public accounts committee (see page 14).
www.nao.org.uk

Health overview and scrutiny committees (HOSCs)
The Health and Social Care Act 2001 gave local authorities specific powers to scrutinise local health services and health organisations. These powers formally rest with authorities that have social care responsibilities (county, unitary, metropolitan, London borough authorities), but there are provisions for joint or delegated scrutiny with borough or district councils.

HOSCs are made up of elected council members not on the authority's executive or cabinet. They are able to call chief executives of local health organisations to attend a scrutiny hearing at least twice a year. HOSCs can:
• refer contested service changes to the Secretary of State
• report their recommendations locally
• insist on being consulted by the NHS over major changes to health services.

The Government is giving local authorities greater discretion over how they exercise their health scrutiny powers, and they will be able to decide for themselves whether to continue with HOSCs, though it is expected many will. For the first time local authority scrutiny of health services will be extended to all providers of NHS care and treatment, including the private sector and primary care practitioners such as GPs, dentists, pharmacists and opticians.

The Centre for Public Scrutiny has helped to foster local authorities' role in scrutinising health services.

Further information
Health overview and scrutiny: exploiting opportunities at a time of change, CfPS, November 2011.
Centre for Public Scrutiny: **www.cfps.org.uk**

Professional regulation

NHS patients need to know that the staff who care for them are well trained and competent. Professional self-regulation has been a cornerstone of the NHS since it began, yet events in the last 15 years – such as the deaths of child heart patients in Bristol (1998–2001), the Alder Hey cases in which organs from dead children were retained without their families' knowledge (2001), Dr Harold Shipman's conviction for multiple murders (2000) and failures in patient care at Mid Staffordshire NHS Foundation Trust (2005–09) – highlighted the need for reform.

Professional regulation covers education, registration, training, continuing professional development and revalidation. It includes setting standards for deciding who should enter and remain members of a profession and determining their fitness to practise. Its underpinning principles are:
• clarity about standards
• maintaining public confidence
• transparency in tackling fitness to practise
• responsiveness to and protection of patients.

Professional regulation issues and initiatives are usually UK-wide.

Spotlight on policy: registration and licensing

The Care Quality Commission and Monitor are to operate a single, integrated process of registration and licensing for all health and social care services in England.

Since 2010 all providers of certain health and social care services have had to register with the CQC and demonstrate that they meet a single set of essential standards for quality and safety of care. The standards are grouped into six areas:
• involvement and information
• personalised care, treatment and support
• safeguarding and safety
• suitability of staffing
• quality and management
• suitability of management.

Without registering, it is illegal for organisations to provide certain services, and to maintain their registration, providers must demonstrate a continuing ability to meet all the standards.

As part of Monitor's role as sector regulator, it is developing a licence for all providers of NHS-funded services, which will stipulate conditions with which licence-holders will have to comply. These will relate to different aspects of healthcare regulation than those relevant to CQC registration, but a key requirement will be that providers are registered with the CQC. Monitor will have powers to ensure providers comply with their licence conditions. The first licences are expected to be granted to foundation trusts in December 2012. All other providers will be eligible for licences from April 2013.

Further information

Essential standards of quality and safety: guidance about compliance, CQC, March 2010.
Developing the new NHS provider licence: a framework document, Monitor, November 2011.

Milestones in reforming professional regulation

Since 2001, developments in professional regulation have included:

2001 New multi-professional Health Professions Council
Reform of the Dentists Act 1984

2002 New Nursing and Midwifery Council
Overhaul of GMC structure and fitness-to-practise process

2003 Council for Healthcare Regulatory Excellence (CHRE) established
Introduction of statutory regulation for operating department practitioners
European Qualifications Regulations

2004 Further overhaul of GMC structure and fitness-to-practise process

2005 Reform of the Opticians Act 1989

2007 Reform of pharmacy regulation
Reform of the GMC's registration processes
Trust, assurance and safety white paper published

2008 Health and Social Care Act white paper proposals taken forward

2009 Introduction of GMC licence to practise
Practitioner psychologists regulated by HPC

2010 Launch of the General Pharmaceutical Council

2011 Proposal to devolve more power to regulators

2012 Revalidation of doctors to be implemented
Abolition of General Social Care Council and transfer of responsibilities to Health Professions Council
CHRE becomes the Professional Standards Authority for Health and Social Care.

Professional regulatory bodies

During the past decade and especially since reforms in 2008, regulatory bodies have become smaller, with many more public and patient representatives. They have striven for faster, more transparent procedures and more meaningful accountability to the public and the health service. They have also developed common systems across the professions and agreed standards that put patients' interests first. Professional regulatory bodies must be open and make improvements based on feedback from patients, their representatives and the public. They must deal with complaints quickly, thoroughly, objectively and in a way that is responsive to the complainant while treating fairly the health professional complained against.

Updated regulatory bodies have been introduced for medicine, nursing, midwifery and health visiting, the allied health professions and pharmacy:

- The General Medical Council is the regulatory body for doctors. It receives about 5,000 complaints a year, of which about 1,700 result in investigation. Since 2009, all doctors must be both registered and hold a licence to practise; they must renew their licence periodically through revalidation (see page 155).

  www.gmc-uk.org

- The Nursing and Midwifery Council replaced the UK Central Council in 2002 as the body responsible for governing nurses, midwives and health visitors.

  www.nmc-uk.org

- The Health Professions Council is responsible for the professions previously regulated by the Council for Professions Supplementary to Medicine, and includes groups of healthcare professionals not previously covered by formal statutory regulation.

  www.hpc-uk.org

NHS CONFEDERATION

- The General Dental Council and General Optical Council regulate the dental and optometry professions.
  GDC www.gdc-uk.org
  GOC www.optical.org
- The General Pharmaceutical Council replaced the Royal Pharmaceutical Society of Great Britain in 2010 as the regulator for pharmacists and pharmacy technicians.
  www.pharmacyregulation.org

Reforming professional regulation

The coalition Government believes the system of professional regulation has grown 'increasingly complex and expensive and requires continuous government intervention to keep it up to date'. More generally, reducing regulation is a key government priority. A white paper, *Enabling excellence*, proposes:

- to allow regulators to decide for themselves how they carry out their duties, without approval from the Privy Council or DH
- to constrain the growth and costs of the regulatory system, beginning with a review of cost efficiency and effectiveness and a freeze on registration fees
- voluntary registration for professions or occupations not regulated by law, such as some healthcare scientists, psychotherapists and counsellors, with incentives for employers to use workers on voluntary registers
- simplifying the legislation governing regulators
- simplifying the structure by abolishing the General Social Care Council and making the Professional Standards Authority for Health and Social Care (formerly the CHRE) more independent and self-funding.

In addition, the four UK health departments agreed that from April 2012 the Health Professions Council should hold a statutory register of practitioners who supply unlicensed herbal medicines.

Further information

Enabling excellence: autonomy and accountability for healthcare workers, social workers and social care workers, TSO, February 2011.

Spotlight on policy: revalidation of doctors

Revalidation is the process by which doctors have to demonstrate to the GMC, normally every five years, that they are up to date and fit to practise. It is a new way of regulating the medical profession that will focus on doctors' efforts to maintain and improve their practice. Revalidation is to be introduced in late 2012, but has a long history, being first proposed by the GMC in 2000.

It will be based on a local evaluation of doctors' performance through an annual appraisal, at which a portfolio of supporting information – such as feedback from patients and colleagues and patient outcomes – is used as a basis for discussion. Information from the appraisal will be provided to a 'responsible officer' – for example, a trust medical director – who will recommend to the GMC whether to revalidate the doctor.

The NHS medical director says: 'The process is vital for engaging doctors with organisational ambition, promoting continuous professional development, clinical quality improvement and identifying early potential problems with clinical service delivery. It facilitates personal and organisational development.'

Further information

Revalidation: a statement of intent, DH, Scottish Government, Welsh Government, Northern Ireland Department of Health, Social Services and Public Safety and GMC, October 2010.

Revalidation of doctors: fourth report of session 2010–11, House of Commons health committee, February 2011.

Briefing 85: Medical revalidation: what employers need to know, NHS Employers, November 2011.

NHS Revalidation Support Team **www.revalidationsupport.nhs.uk**

Code of conduct for NHS managers

Just as doctors, nurses and other health workers have codified ethics, so since 2002 have NHS managers. Written by senior managers in collaboration with the DH, the code states that all NHS managers must:

- make the care and safety of patients their first concern and act to protect them from risk
- respect the public, patients, relatives, carers, NHS staff and partners in other agencies

- be honest and act with integrity
- accept responsibility for their own work and the proper performance of the people they manage
- show their commitment to working as a team member by working with all their colleagues in the NHS and the wider community
- take responsibility for their own learning and development.

NHS organisations must incorporate the code in the contracts of chief executives and directors, and investigate alleged breaches. Those who break the code can be dismissed from the NHS and barred from re-employment within it.

A DH advisory group concluded in 2010 that the code and other existing measures were insufficient to guarantee the calibre of NHS managers. It recommended clarifying standards; strengthening recruitment, vetting and employment procedures; enhancing corporate governance; and considering a system of licensing, accrediting or regulating managers.

Further information
Code of conduct for NHS managers, DH, October 2002.
Assuring the quality of senior NHS managers: report of the advisory group on assuring the quality of senior NHS managers, DH, February 2010.
www.nhsemployers.org/managementstandards

07 Financing the NHS

While the NHS has embraced diversity in the provision of its services, its funding continues to draw overwhelmingly on a single source – taxation – although it does raise a certain amount from charges. However, the way money flows through the system has been drastically reformed with the gradual introduction of 'payment by results' since 2003. NHS funding increases ran at record levels for five years until 2008/09, and had always been planned to be much slower after that. Now, however, despite a government commitment to increase the NHS budget in real terms until 2015, with growth at a mere 0.1 per cent it is under great pressure. It therefore needs to secure the maximum gains from improved efficiency and productivity if it is to continue to meet rising demand.

Sources of funding

Taxation

Funding healthcare through taxation ensures universal access to services irrespective of ability to pay. About three-quarters of NHS funding in England comes from general taxation – the Consolidated Fund – and just under a fifth from the NHS element of national insurance.

The health service is the second biggest single item of public expenditure (after social security payments), and absorbs 18 per cent of money raised through tax and national insurance contributions (NICs).

General taxation is generally regarded as being a highly efficient way of financing healthcare: it means the Government has both a strong incentive and the capacity to control costs; administrative costs especially tend to be low. As taxation draws revenue from a wide base, it helps minimise distortions in particular sectors of the economy. The social insurance element of NHS financing in the form of NICs paid by employees and employers, although relatively small, has been found to be highly progressive – what people pay directly reflects what they can afford.

However, financing healthcare through taxation means the overall level of resources is constrained by what the Government judges the economy can afford and what is electorally viable, while choices between what services are and are not provided are made centrally. Many would argue that in the past the UK system has gone too far in controlling expenditure, leading to under-investment in the NHS compared with other countries over many years. The degree of individual choice available to patients has tended to be relatively limited, although current policy is trying to address this.

Charges

The NHS currently charges for a limited number of clinical services – in England mainly prescriptions, dental treatments, sight tests, glasses and contact lenses. These out-of-pocket payments account for about 2 per cent of NHS funding. The principle remains that they should be paid only by those who can afford them, so those who cannot are not discouraged from seeking advice and treatment. A wide range of exemptions applies, including in most cases young and elderly people and those who are unemployed or on low incomes.

Prescriptions, dental treatment, sight tests

Since April 2012, prescription charges in England have been £7.65 per item. NHS Wales abolished prescription charges in 2007 and NHSScotland in 2011. Prescription charges in Northern Ireland were abolished in 2010, but their reintroduction is now being considered. Complete abolition has been ruled out in England as it would reduce NHS revenue by about £450 million, but charges for cancer patients were ended in 2009. It is estimated that about 50 per cent of the population of England does not have to pay prescription charges. About 89 per cent of prescription items are dispensed free to patients.

Most courses of dental treatment cost £17.50 or £48, depending on their complexity. The maximum charge for complex dental treatment is £209. Sight test charges vary but are usually between £17 and £30, although they have been free in Scotland since 2006.

In addition, there are currently limited charges for non-clinical services such as single maternity rooms and car parking. NHSScotland abolished hospital car-parking charges at the beginning of 2009, and in Northern Ireland car-parking charges have been abolished for seriously ill patients and their families. The coalition Government has rejected the idea of mandatory free parking for the NHS in England – which would have cost up to £200 million – though the previous Labour Government had consulted on it.

Further information

NHS car parking: response to consultation, DH, September 2010.

Recovering the costs of personal injury

Since the 1930s hospitals have been entitled by law to collect money for treating road traffic accident victims from drivers' insurance companies. Since 2007 the NHS has been able to recover costs from insurance companies for treating patients in all cases where personal injury compensation is paid. In the first nine months of 2011/12, the injury costs recovery scheme raised £158 million in England, Scotland and Wales. The Compensation Recovery Unit, part of the Department for Work and Pensions, collects the charges on the DH's behalf. They are:

- use of an NHS ambulance: £185
- flat rate for treatment without admission: £615
- daily rate for treatment with admission: £755
- maximum in any one case: £45,153.

Further information

Injury costs recovery scheme, DH, January 2007.
Compensation Recovery Unit **www.dwp.gov.uk/cru**

Overseas visitors

Anyone who is lawfully 'ordinarily resident' in the UK is entitled to free NHS treatment in England, regardless of nationality. UK residents may be absent from the country for up to six months in a year before being considered for charges for NHS hospital treatment. British citizens who do not normally live in the UK may have to pay charges for NHS treatment, regardless of whether they have paid UK taxes and national insurance contributions, unless they are eligible for certain exemptions. British state pensioners who split their time between the UK and another European Economic Area member state are exempt from charges. Responsibility for deciding who is entitled to free treatment rests with the hospital providing the treatment.

Asylum seekers whose application for refuge in the UK is outstanding are entitled to use NHS services without charge, as are those refused asylum but unable to return home due to 'recognised barriers' (see page 103). Unaccompanied children, including those in local authority care, are also exempt from charges. In any case, treatment in an A&E department or walk-in centre, family planning services, compulsory psychiatric treatment and treatment for certain communicable diseases are free to all.

Despite a 2009 review, the Government believes the system is still 'too complex, generous and inconsistently applied', and is conducting another review. In the meantime, anyone owing the NHS £1,000 or more will not be allowed to come to or stay in the UK until the debt is paid off. It is hoped this will capture 94 per cent of outstanding charges owed to the NHS.

Further information
Access to the NHS by foreign nationals – Government response to the consultation, March 2011.
Guidance on implementing the overseas visitors hospital charging regulations, DH, June 2011.

Other sources
Other sources of NHS funding come from land sales and income generation schemes. In addition, the Big Lottery Fund has provided funding for health (as well as education and the environment). UK-wide it distributed £300 million to help set up healthy living centres, and gave over £360 million for coronary heart disease, stroke and cancer services. It also allocated £84 million for palliative care and support and information services for people with cancer and other life-threatening conditions.

Further information
www.biglotteryfund.org.uk

Resource allocation
The Treasury is responsible for overall public expenditure. It periodically conducts a spending review of all government departments (see page 106), after which departments – including the DH – draw up structural reform plans, setting out what they expect to provide with their new resources. The DH in turn issues priorities and planning guidance to the NHS in the annual operating framework. The Treasury makes block grants to the Scottish Parliament, Welsh Assembly and the Northern Ireland Assembly, from which they allocate funds for the NHS.

In 2012/13 the DH allocated resources to primary care trusts for the last time. In future the NHS Commissioning Board will allocate resources to clinical commissioning groups (CCGs), while the DH will make grants to local authorities for their public health responsibilities.

The Board will calculate practice-level budgets and allocate these directly to CCGs, which will be responsible for managing the combined commissioning budgets of their member practices. The DH is working with its Advisory Committee on Resource Allocation (ACRA) to develop an allocation formula based on practice-level allocations.

Spotlight on policy: payment by results

In a far-reaching change to the way money flows through the NHS in England between commissioners and providers, a system of payment by results has been gradually introduced. The aim is to ensure funding follows the patient, to underpin policy on increasing patient choice between a variety of providers.

The intention is to provide a transparent system for paying trusts which encourages activity and so helps keep waiting times short. Commissioners purchase the volume of activity they require for their populations, but instead of drawing up block agreements with trusts as previously, providers are paid for the activity they undertake. A tariff derived from national reference costs removed prices from local negotiation, so that commissioners focused instead on gains in patient choice, quality, shorter waiting time, volumes of activity and efficiency.

Payment by results began in a limited way in 2003/04, and has been gradually extended. Each year, changes to the tariff are 'sense-checked' for anomalies that could lead to perverse incentives and 'road-tested' before their introduction to enable the service to get used to the new tariff.

A code of conduct for payment by results sets out core principles, ground rules for organisational behaviour and expectations of how the system should operate – and is intended to minimise disputes.

In 2010/11 'best practice tariffs' to encourage and reimburse the costs of high-quality care were introduced for four high-volume areas with significant unexplained variation in practice.

For 2012/13, tariff prices have been reduced by 1.5 per cent, with a 4 per cent efficiency requirement offsetting pay and price inflation of 2.2 per cent. For certain conditions, commissioners no longer have to pay for emergency readmissions within 30 days of discharge from an acute hospital. Payment by results will see a 'significant expansion', the DH says: in particular, it will be extended into mental health services during 2012/13. It will also be used to strengthen the link between payment and quality and encourage integration of care.

Further information
Briefing 211: The impact of non-payment for acute readmissions, NHS Confederation/ Foundation Trust Network, February 2011.
A simple guide to payment by results, DH, July 2011.
Payment by results guidance for 2012–13, DH, February 2012.
Code of conduct for payment by results in 2012–13, DH, February 2012.

Traditionally, four factors have been taken into account in allocating resources:
- weighted capitation targets – set according to a national formula, which calculated a PCT's target share of resources based on its population and their health needs due to deprivation or high mortality and morbidity levels, as well as a 'market forces factor' to account for unavoidable geographical variations in the cost of providing services; the intention was that every PCT should be able to commission similar levels of health services for populations in similar need
- recurrent baselines – representing the actual allocation a PCT received in the previous allocation round, plus any recurrent adjustments
- distance from target – the difference between target and recurrent baseline
- pace-of-change policy – decided by ministers for each allocation round, this determined the level of increase all PCTs got and the extra for under-target PCTs to move them closer to their weighted capitation targets.

It is expected that any new allocation formula will take similar considerations into account, as the Board will have a duty to reduce inequalities in access to services and in patient outcomes. It will have the power to adjust CCG allocations in future years to reflect previous overspends or underspends, similar to the way that PCT allocations operated, to give incentives for good financial management.

Capital

Capital investment is expenditure – typically on buildings or large items of equipment – that will continue to provide benefits into the future. To count as NHS capital, spending must generally be on assets that individually cost £5,000 or more and are recorded on the balance sheet as fixed assets.

The NHS's main sources of capital are government funds, receipts from land sales and the private finance initiative. The NHS Commissioning Board will set capital limits for each clinical commissioning group.

Vital statistics: NHS capital spending plans 2010–15 (£ million)

	2010/11	2011/12	2012/13	2013/14	2014/15
Amount	5,122	4,429	4,429	4,437	4,648
Real growth %	-	-15.18	-2.22	-2.38	2.05

Annual average real growth: -4.66%
Cumulative growth over four years: -17.38%

Source: Department of Health

Foundation trusts are free to reinvest all cash generated from their activities to maintain and replace their assets. They may also borrow capital, from commercial banks or the DH, under 'prudential borrowing' arrangements if their projections of future cash flows show they would be able to afford to pay back the sum with interest. Monitor assigns each foundation trust a 'prudential borrowing limit', fixing the amount of debt it may take on.

Private finance initiative (PFI)

PFI involves a public–private partnership between an NHS organisation and a private sector consortium that makes private capital available for health service projects.

The private sector consortium will usually include a construction company, a funding organisation and a facilities management provider. Contracts for major PFI schemes may be for 30 years or more and are typically DBFO (design, build, finance and operate) projects. This means the private sector partner is responsible for:
• designing the facilities (based on the requirements specified by the NHS)
• building the facilities (to time and at a fixed cost)
• financing the capital cost (with the return to be recovered through continuing to make the facilities available and meeting NHS requirements)
• operating the facilities (providing facilities management and other support services).

One aim of PFI is to reduce the overall risks associated with procuring new assets and services for the NHS, as well as to improve the quality and cost-effectiveness of public services. But critics questioned whether PFI will really provide long-term value for money for the NHS, and claimed services have been cut in some cases to make schemes affordable. The House of Commons Treasury committee found PFI projects in the NHS to be 'inherently inflexible', while the public accounts committee concluded:

'Whilst PFI has delivered many new hospitals … which might otherwise not have been delivered, there is no clear evidence of whether PFI is any better or worse value for money than other procurement routes.' It added: 'There are, however, wide and unexplained variations in the cost of hospital support services, such as cleaning, catering and portering.'

By the end of 2010, of the PFI schemes that had been approved since 1997:
• 94 were operational
• 8 were under construction
• 5 were in procurement or preparation.

Of schemes funded by public capital:
• 33 were operational
• 2 were under construction
• 5 were in procurement or preparation.

The DH has offered seven NHS trusts with structural financial issues and large PFI schemes access to £1.5 billion in aid over 25 years, provided they can pass key tests to show they are achieving productivity savings and low waiting times and have a plan to manage resources better in future.

Under the previous Labour Government, all major NHS capital projects were expected to consider whether PFI could represent a value-for-money solution. The Treasury is currently undertaking a 'fundamental reassessment' of PFI and considering alternatives. Its aim is to create a model which is cheaper, accesses a wider range of private sector financing sources and strikes a better balance of risk between the private and the public sectors.

Further information
PFI in housing and hospitals: fourteenth report of session 2010–11, House of Commons public accounts committee, January 2011.
Private finance initiative: seventeenth report of session 2010–12, House of Commons Treasury committee, July 2011.
Lessons from PFI and other projects: forty-fourth report of session 2010–12, House of Commons public accounts committee, July 2011.

NHS Local Improvement Finance Trust (LIFT)

NHS LIFT aims to encourage investment in primary care and community-based facilities with the aim of refurbishing or replacing them. It is similar to PFI, except that it is a joint venture between the NHS, the private sector partner, local authorities and GPs.

Community Health Partnerships (CHP), a public–private partnership between the DH and Partnerships UK, was set up to invest money in NHS LIFT and help attract additional private funding; the DH became the sole owner in 2006. At local level, NHS LIFT is not a single trust but a series of local public–private partnerships between the NHS, the private sector, CHP and local authorities. The resulting partnership is a LIFT company, which is a local joint venture.

More than 300 new community facilities have either opened or are under construction as part of the LIFT programme, which seeks investment in primary care developments by bundling them together. So far, 49 local LIFT schemes are renting accommodation to GPs, pharmacists, opticians, dentists and others on a lease basis. Schemes may now include clinical and facilities management services as well as buildings and maintenance. The total value of the LIFT programme is over £2.5 billion.

Express LIFT, introduced in 2009, reduces the time and cost of setting up a scheme by offering a choice of seven pre-approved partners for local procurements by the NHS and local authorities, completing contracts within three or four months rather than two years.

Further information

Celebrating a transformation of local health and community infrastructure, Community Health Partnerships, July 2010.
www.communityhealthpartnerships.co.uk

NHS spending

The era of growth

From the time the NHS was founded until the end of the 1990s, its annual average increase in funding was just over 3 per cent – slightly more than the real growth in the economy as a whole. However, from the early 1980s, real spending changes were erratic. Taking into account the level of inflation in the NHS rather than in the general economy, annual average growth was about 0.9 per cent from 1983 to 1987, 2 per cent from 1987 to 1992 and 1.4 per cent from 1992 to 1997. In 2000 the Government announced its intention to raise the share of national income spent on health to the European average: it then ranked 14th out of the 15 EU countries.

In 2001 Derek Wanless, former chief executive of NatWest Bank, was commissioned to produce the first evidence-based assessment of the NHS's long-term resource requirements. He produced a similar report for NHS Wales in 2003, while in Northern Ireland the Appleby Report of 2005 (see page 236) sought to predict future needs and resources.

As a result of Wanless's report on the English NHS, the 2002 Budget heralded the largest sustained increases in any five-year period in NHS history: an annual average increase of 7.4 per cent in real terms between 2002/03 and 2007/08, a total increase of 43 per cent in real terms over the period. The aim was to put the health service on a 'sound long-term financial footing', making significant investment in IT, buildings and equipment, and raising NHS spending to the EU average. To help pay for these increases, national insurance contributions were raised by 1 per cent from April 2003. NHS spending was long planned to increase at a slower rate for three years from 2008/09. Overall, between 2000/01 and 2010/11, the NHS enjoyed annual real terms growth in revenue of 5.3 per cent.

NHS revenue since 2000/01 (England)

	REVENUE SPENDING (£ BILLION)	REAL GROWTH %
2000/01	42.7	-
2001/02	47.3	8.4
2002/03	51.9	6.4
2003/04	61.9	8.8
2004/05	66.9	5.2
2005/06	74.2	8.9
2006/07	78.5	2.4
2007/08	86.4	7.0
2008/09	90.7	2.2
2009/10	97.8	6.1
2010/11	98.9	0.5
2011/12	102.6	0.2
2012/13	105.2	0.0
2013/14	108.2	0.1
2014/15	111.1	0.0

Source: Department of Health

The era of restraint

Since the financial crisis in 2008, the subsequent world recession and the UK's burgeoning deficit, public finances have been under huge pressure. The NHS chief executive said in 2009: 'We are at a critical juncture in the history of the NHS. After a decade of investment and reform that has helped drive real improvements for our patients, the NHS, along with other public services, is about to enter perhaps the toughest financial climate it has ever known.'

As a result, the NHS committed to finding an unprecedented £15–20 billion in efficiency savings between 2010 and 2015 under its quality, innovation, productivity and prevention (QIPP) programme (see page 170). Known as the 'Nicholson challenge' after the NHS chief executive who launched it in 2009, this is not intended to cut budgets or reduce services but improve productivity: the NHS must derive £15–20 billion more value from its resources during a period when budget increases will not keep pace with rising demand. QIPP was predicted to achieve £5.9 billion of savings by the end of 2011/12. Its target is to achieve £10 billion by 2012/13.

MPs on the Commons health committee noted these savings could only be achieved by making 'fundamental changes' to the way care is delivered, otherwise 'inefficiency and poor quality' would result. But in early 2012 they reported that measures so far introduced were often 'short-term expedients' or 'salami-slicing'. They said: 'We have the impression that NHS organisations are making do and squeezing savings from existing services simply to get through the first year of the programme. We heard little to persuade us that this overriding need to do things differently is being planned for in future years and we are convinced that the required level of efficiency gain will not be achieved without significant change in the care model.'

On coming to power in 2010, the coalition Government pledged to protect DH funding (a promise made to only one other department) despite its overriding priority of cutting public spending to reduce the deficit. The spending review settlement (see page 106) envisaged a 0.4 per cent real-terms increase in overall NHS funding between 2010/11 and 2014/15; although revenue will rise by a small amount, capital spending will fall by 17 per cent. In addition, the NHS will make £1 billion a year available for social care. The Chancellor's Autumn Statement in 2011 made it clear that financial restraint would continue beyond the end of the current spending review period until at least 2016/17.

Spending review settlement for the NHS (£ million)

	2010/11	2011/12	2012/13	2013/14	2014/15
Revenue	99,760	102,621	105,170	108,158	111,059
Capital	5,122	4,429	4,429	4,437	4,648
Total	103,781	105,909	108,417	111,371	114,439

*Total allows deductions for depreciation

Real growth (%)

		2011/12	2012/13	2013/14	2014/15
Revenue		0.9	0.2	0.22	0.03
Capital		-15.18	-2.22	-2.38	2.05

Annual average real growth (%)
Revenue: 0.34
Capital: -4.66

Cumulative growth over 4 years (%)
Revenue: 1.36
Capital: -17.38

Source: Department of Health

Further information

Spending review 2010, HM Treasury, October 2010.
Public expenditure: second report of session 2010–11, House of Commons health committee, December 2010.
Autumn Statement 2011, HM Treasury, November 2011.
Public expenditure: thirteenth report of session 2010–12, House of Commons health committee, January 2012.

Buying goods and services

Meeting the drugs bill: value-based pricing

Since 1957 the Pharmaceutical Price Regulation Scheme has regulated the prices of branded medicines and the profits that manufacturers are allowed to make on their sales to the NHS. It has produced a series of voluntary agreements between the DH and the pharmaceutical industry, each lasting about five years. The PPRS is a UK-wide scheme, and covers around 80 per cent by value of the medicines used in the NHS in both primary and secondary care. The total NHS drugs bill in England is almost £12 billion a year.

From 2014, the Government plans to replace the PPRS with 'value-based pricing' of branded medicines. Currently, drug companies set prices for branded drugs within the framework of the PPRS, and NICE (see page 148)

Spotlight on policy: quality, innovation, productivity and prevention (QIPP)

The QIPP programme aims to achieve major efficiency savings by redesigning services and improving productivity without compromising quality. It is focusing on three key areas divided into workstreams, each led by NHS and DH experts. These are:

Commissioning and pathways
- safe care
- right care
- long-term conditions
- urgent and emergency care
- end-of-life care

Provider efficiency
- back-office efficiency and optimal management
- procurement
- clinical support
- productive care
- medicines use and procurement

System enablers
- primary care commissioning.

Each NHS organisation has developed its own QIPP plans. QIPP was begun under the previous Labour Government, and the current Government's *Liberating the NHS* white paper promised QIPP would 'continue with even greater urgency'. Savings on pay, management and administration are expected to yield about 40 per cent of the target and service changes about 20 per cent. The remaining 40 per cent is expected to come from use of the payment-by-results tariff in the acute sector (see page 162).

Further information
Delivering efficiency savings in the NHS: briefing for the House of Commons health committee, NAO, September 2011.

recommends whether the drug is clinically and cost-effective. Under the new system, the price of a drug to the NHS will be based on an assessment of its value.

Vital statistics: NHS spending 2010/2011 (£ billion)

Primary care

1 GP services: 7.68
2 Prescribing costs: 8.28
3 Dental services: 2.82
4 General ophthalmic services: 0.48
5 Pharmaceutical services: 1.93
6 Other: 0.18
   Total: 21.37

Source: Department of Health

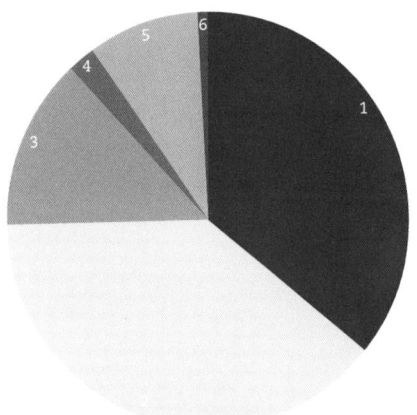

Secondary care

1 Learning difficulties: 2.58
2 Mental illness: 8.37
3 Maternity: 2.53
4 General and acute: 38.91
5 Accident and emergency: 2.22
6 Community health services: 8.40
7 Other: 3.09
   Total: 66.10

Source: Department of Health

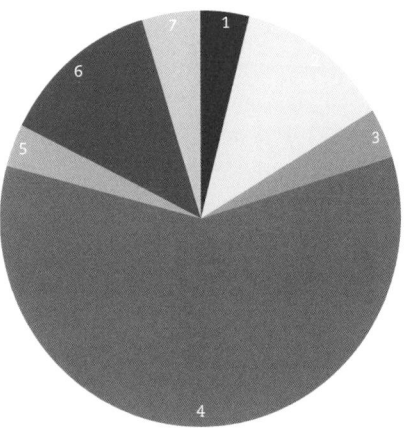

The Government hopes to design a 'stable and transparent' system that enables companies to predict in advance how prospective products may fare, and to focus their research on treatments that society values most. It will not renegotiate the scheme every five years, as with the PPRS. A medicine's value will be influenced by, for example, the severity of the condition it is intended to treat and the level of unmet need, as well as the scale of therapeutic innovation and improvement it represents.

If a drug's price was higher than justified by the value-based pricing assessment, the Government would ask the company to lower its price or produce evidence to justify the value. If the company refused, it would have to explain to the public why it was not prepared to offer that drug at an appropriate price.

Value-based pricing will apply to new drugs placed on the market from January 2014. Those already on the market will be covered by new parallel arrangements. As well as drugs subject to value-based pricing, the NHS will have to fund those already recommended by NICE: patients will continue to have the legal right to clinically appropriate, cost-effective drugs and treatments, as set out in the NHS Constitution.

As an interim measure, the Government set up a cancer drugs fund in 2010, which will run until value-based pricing is introduced. This is making available £200 million a year to increase access to innovative but expensive new drugs that extend life or improve quality of life.

Value-based pricing will apply to branded and not generic medicines. A maximum price scheme for generics – on which the NHS spends more than £2 billion a year – was introduced in 2000 to restrain the drugs bill after steep price rises, saving around £330 million a year. Since 2004, where there is a limited number of manufacturers of a generic medicine or the supply is concentrated, manufacturers have to seek the DH's agreement to any price increase. Manufacturers and wholesalers must submit quarterly information on income revenues, cost of purchases and volumes of transactions.

Further information

A new value-based approach to the pricing of branded medicines: a consultation, DH, December 2010.

The cancer drugs fund: guidance to support operation of the cancer drugs fund in 2011–12, DH, March 2011.

A new value-based approach to the pricing of branded medicines: Government response to consultation, DH, July 2011.

NHS Shared Business Services

NHS Shared Business Services was launched as a joint venture between the DH and a private sector company in 2005, building on an earlier shared financial services initiative that used two purpose-built centres in Leeds and Bristol. SBS provides finance and accounting, payroll, human resources and procurement services so that frontline organisations can concentrate on patient care. It currently provides services to over 40 per cent of NHS organisations. With 1,200 employees at eight locations in England and 550 staff in India, it processes 4.5 million transactions a year.
www.sbs.nhs.uk

NHS Business Services Authority

This special health authority was set up in 2006 to be the main processing facility for payment, reimbursement, remuneration and reconciliation for NHS patients, employees and others. For example, it manages the NHS Pension Scheme, reimburses dentists and pharmacists, and administers the European health insurance card in the UK. It was formed from the Dental Practice Board, NHS Pensions Agency and the Prescription Pricing Authority.
www.nhsbsa.nhs.uk

NHS Supply Chain

NHS Supply Chain is a single organisation that provides procurement, logistics, e-commerce and customer and supplier support. Its 2,400 staff buy and deliver over 500,000 products for more than 1,000 healthcare organisations. It aims to save £1.2 billion for the NHS, and is operated by DHL under a ten-year contract with the NHS Business Services Authority.
www.supplychain.nhs.uk

Commercial support units

Regional CSUs are centres of expertise providing commercial support to commissioners and providers, managing contracts and working with NHS Supply Chain to secure better value for money for goods and services bought by the NHS. CSUs were set up at a cost of £20 million in 2010. They are intended to give healthcare suppliers a single, simple point of contact with the NHS.

NHS Protect

NHS Protect leads work to protect NHS staff and resources from crime. It has national responsibility for tackling fraud, violence, bribery, corruption, criminal damage, theft and other unlawful action such as market-fixing. It also leads work on NHS emergency and counter-terrorism preparedness, national data analysis and risk assessment, anti-fraud and pro-security research. In addition, it provides NHS anti-fraud services to the Welsh Government.

www.nhsbsa.nhs.uk/Protect

08 Staffing and human resources

As the UK's largest employer – indeed, one of the largest employers in the world – the NHS attaches special importance to good human resources policy and practice. Staff costs account for about 75 per cent of hospital expenditure. Effective recruitment, retention and remuneration of a well-trained and well-motivated workforce are seen as crucial factors in achieving ambitions for patient care.

The era of funding growth saw significant expansion in the NHS workforce and revised contracts to reflect changing patterns of care. Improving staff productivity and efficiency as spending diminishes is now a key theme. Organisations must also do their utmost to engage staff in designing ways of improving services. NHS commitments to staff and their responsibilities form a major part of the NHS Constitution (see page 184).

Workforce planning

In future the DH will have progressively less direct involvement in planning and development of the healthcare workforce, in line with the Government's policy of devolving responsibility for decision-making as close to the front line as possible. In its *Liberating the NHS* white paper, it said: 'We cannot continue to expect top-down workforce planning to respond to the bottom-up changes in patterns of service' that clinical commissioning groups will instigate. A new national body, Health Education England (HEE), is being created, while local education and training boards (LETBs) will be set up to articulate local needs. The Government expects to see healthcare providers with local clinical leadership take a lead role in planning and developing their workforce.

Health Education England

HEE will oversee workforce planning, education and training, as well as supporting local arrangements for planning and commissioning education and training. It will take over the functions of Medical Education England (which currently covers medicine, dentistry, pharmacy and healthcare science), the allied health professional advisory board and the nursing and midwifery professional advisory board.

HEE's purpose will be to ensure the health workforce has the right skills and is available in the right numbers. Key functions will be:
• providing national leadership on planning and developing the workforce
• authorising and supporting development of local education and training boards (see opposite)

- promoting education and training responsive to changing needs, including responsibility for recruiting medical trainees
- allocating and accounting for NHS education and training resources and the outcomes achieved
- ensuring the supply of the professionally qualified clinical workforce.

HEE's main focus will be on professionally qualified staff whose education and training is funded through the £4.9 billion multi-professional education and training budget. HEE will be accountable to the Secretary of State, and have about 150 staff, a chief executive, a board chair and at least five non-executive members. It will be established as a special health authority in June 2012 with a view to beginning work from October, becoming fully operational in April 2013.

As healthcare education and training are developed and regulated UK-wide, HEE will need to build strong links with its equivalent organisations in Scotland, Wales and Northern Ireland to ensure consistency across the country.

Local education and training boards

LETBs will enable NHS employers, education providers and health professionals to work together to plan and commission education and training. They will have flexibility to support local priorities in innovation and workforce development. Their functions will include:
- developing a skills and development strategy for the local health workforce
- collecting local workforce data and plans
- accounting for education and training funding allocated by HEE
- securing the quality of education and training programmes
- supporting access to continuing professional development
- working in partnership with universities, clinical academics, other education providers and those investing in research and innovation
- working with local authorities and health and wellbeing boards
- working with HEE to develop national strategy and priorities.

LETBs have been promised local autonomy, subject to following HEE's national strategic direction.

Centre for Workforce Intelligence

The Centre for Workforce Intelligence (CfWI) provides expert advice and information on workforce planning and development to the health and social care system nationally and locally. It undertakes horizon-scanning to identify future risks and opportunities for the workforce. It will support HEE in providing national oversight and leadership on workforce planning and on commissioning education and training. CfWI will also advise LETBs on their workforce plans, and provide information to the DH and HEE to inform resource allocation.

www.cfwi.org.uk

Further information

Liberating the NHS: developing the healthcare workforce – from design to delivery, DH, January 2012.

Education and training – next stage: a report from the NHS Future Forum, NHS Future Forum, January 2012.

Vital statistics: NHS staff numbers (September 2011)

The annual census of staff showed there were 1,350,377 people working for the NHS in England in September 2011 – a decrease of 1.4 per cent on the same time in 2010.

This figure included:
- 143,836 doctors (including 39,088 consultants and 39,780 GPs)
- 370,327 qualified nurses
- 152,216 scientific, therapeutic and technical staff
- 18,687 ambulance staff
- 347,064 clinical support staff
- 219,624 infrastructure support staff.

NHS Employers

The NHS Employers organisation represents employers in the health service in England on workforce issues. It reflects employers' views and acts on their behalf in four priority areas:
• pay and negotiations
• recruitment and planning the workforce
• healthy and productive workplaces
• employment policy and practice.

NHS Employers, set up in 2004, is part of the NHS Confederation. The organisation's vision is to be the authoritative voice of workforce leaders, experts in HR, negotiating fairly to get the best deal for patients.
www.nhsemployers.org

Social Partnership Forum

The NHS Social Partnership Forum, set up in 1998 and revised in 2007 and 2012, brings together NHS trade unions, NHS Employers and the DH to discuss current issues and develop joint initiatives to tackle national problems. It meets twice a year, with a smaller steering group meeting every two months.

Current work priorities are:
• supporting staff through change and transfer
• workforce implications of QIPP (see page 170)
• staff morale and engagement
• strengthening partnership
• responding to emerging issues.

The Forum has produced the NHS Staff Passport toolkit, a guide for staff facing transfer, which includes information on employment standards and rights they can expect when transferring from a job either within the NHS, or from a job within the NHS to another organisation.

Further information
Partnership agreement: an agreement between DH, NHS Employers and NHS trade unions, Social Partnership Forum/DH, February 2012.
www.socialpartnershipforum.org

NHS Careers

NHS Careers is a service providing information on careers in the NHS in England. It consists of a telephone and email helpline, website, literature and supporting services for NHS employers, schools, colleges and careers advisers. Launched in 1999, it aims to raise awareness among the potential future workforce of the 350 careers the NHS offers. It has developed a service for 14–19-year-olds to find out what working in the NHS is like, and another where undergraduates on clinical and non-clinical courses in England can look at their options for a career in the NHS.

www.nhscareers.nhs.uk
www.stepintothenhs.nhs.uk
www.whatcanIdowithmydegree.nhs.uk

NHS Jobs

NHS Jobs is an online recruitment service offering details of job vacancies throughout the NHS in England and Wales. It provides employers with online tools to manage every stage of the recruitment cycle. Each month it carries details of around 20,000 career opportunities in the NHS, attracts 6 million visits and receives job applications from more than 250,000 jobseekers. About 90 per cent of NHS job applications are made through the website. Every NHS trust in England and Wales is registered to advertise with NHS Jobs, which is estimated to have saved the NHS over £240 million in advertising and recruitment administration costs since its launch in 2003.

www.jobs.nhs.uk

Pay and pensions

Pay accounts for about 40 per cent of NHS spending, and 65 to 70 per cent in acute and mental health trusts. The pay and conditions of NHS staff are developed mainly through collective bargaining between the NHS and staff organisations, which also represent staff on a wide range of other employment issues. Most staff are members of trade unions or professional associations, and the NHS seeks 'partnership working' on key employment issues. Most NHS staff organisations have a professional and collective bargaining role. NHS Employers negotiates conditions of service and national contracts with the unions on behalf of employers through the NHS Staff Council, and represents employers' views in the pay review process. GPs are independent self-employed contractors, and the general medical services (GMS) contract (see page 182) is negotiated by the British Medical Association and NHS Employers.

Agenda for Change

Agenda for Change was the most significant reform of NHS pay since the creation of the health service in 1948. It applies to 1.3 million NHS staff across the UK, with the exception of doctors, dentists and the most senior managers.

The system is underpinned by a job evaluation scheme specifically designed for the NHS and by the NHS knowledge and skills framework, which supports personal development and career progression.

Agenda for Change was designed to:
- deliver fair pay for non-medical staff based on the principle of equal pay for work of equal value
- provide better links between pay and career progression through the NHS knowledge and skills framework
- harmonise terms and conditions of service such as annual leave, hours and sick pay, and more recently for work performed in unsocial hours.

Staff are placed in one of nine pay bands on the basis of their knowledge, responsibility, skills and effort needed for the job rather than on the basis of their job title.

The terms and conditions of service for all staff directly employed by NHS organisations under Agenda for Change are set out in the NHS Staff Council's *NHS terms and conditions of service handbook*.

All NHS staff earning more than £21,000 have had their pay frozen for two years since April 2011, a measure announced in the Government's emergency Budget of June 2010. Those earning below that amount receive an annual increase of £250.

Further information

The NHS knowledge and skills framework: essential guide for NHS boards, NHS Employers, 2007.
The NHS knowledge and skills framework (KSF): essential guide for NHS staff, NHS Employers, 2007.
NHS terms and conditions of service handbook, NHS Staff Council, April 2011.
www.nhsemployers.org/agendaforchange

Contract for GPs

A new GP contract for general medical services (GMS) was implemented across the UK in 2004, with annual revisions made after negotiations between NHS Employers and the British Medical Association's General Practitioners Committee (GPC). A recent amendment to the contract stipulates that GP practices must belong to a clinical commissioning group. The contract aims to reward practices for providing high-quality care, improve GPs' working lives and ensure patients benefit from a wider range of services in the community.

The GMS contract will be between the practice and the NHS Commissioning Board (it was formerly held by the PCT) rather than with each GP. This is intended to give practices greater freedom to design services for local needs while encouraging better teamworking and skill-mix.

A key component of the GMS contract is the quality and outcomes framework (QOF) which resources and rewards practices for delivering high-quality care (see page 122).

QOF payments will increasingly reflect the prevalence of long-term health conditions, to help address health inequalities by ensuring proportionately greater funding for practices in deprived areas.

Contracts for other doctors and dentists

The current consultants' contract, introduced in 2003, is designed to provide a more effective system of planning and timetabling consultants' duties and activities for the NHS. It gives NHS employers the ability to manage consultants' time in ways that best meet local service needs and priorities. For consultants, it means greater transparency about the commitments expected of them and greater clarity over the support they need from employers to make the maximum effective contribution to improving patient services.

The current contractual arrangements for doctors in hospital and public health training have been in force since December 2000. Junior doctors' hours have been reduced to levels set in the European Working Time Directive: a maximum of 48 hours per week averaged over 26 weeks.

A new contract for staff grade and associate specialist doctors was agreed in 2008. It applies to 13,000 non-consultant career grade NHS doctors and to all new entrants to the new specialty doctor grade. Annual appraisal, job planning and objective setting are essential components of the new contract.

A salaried dentists' contract was implemented in early 2008. A new single pay spine covers dentists, senior dentists, specialist dentists and managerial dentists. The new pay structure is supported by mandatory annual appraisals and job planning to assist career development.

A new community pharmacy contract was implemented in England in 2005, allowing pharmacies to offer an expanded range of clinical services.

Pensions, retirement and redundancy
All NHS staff automatically become members of the NHS Pension Scheme, but they can choose not to join or leave at any time. The scheme for England and Wales underwent significant changes in 2008. Clear processes and procedures for handling absence and supporting staff through rehabilitation, redeployment or ill health retirements were part of this. About 30,000 staff retire from the NHS every year.

The coalition Government has proposed changes to all public service pension schemes, as recommended by the Independent Public Service Pensions Commission led by Lord Hutton, in order to make them sustainable and to save £2.8 billion by 2014/15. Increases in employee contributions are being phased in over three years from April 2012. Revision to the pension scheme itself is currently under discussion and is expected to be implemented from April 2015.

Redundancy arrangements for all staff directly employed by NHS organisations, except very senior managers and staff covered by the Doctors' and Dentists' Review Body, are included in the *NHS terms and conditions of service handbook*.

Further information
NHS Pension Scheme **www.nhsbsa.nhs.uk/pensions**

The NHS as an employer
The NHS recognises staff as its greatest asset and knows that to recruit and retain the right people it needs to practise excellence in employment. This includes treating staff with respect and supporting them in their work; valuing equality and diversity; ensuring a healthy workplace; offering flexible working; and providing training and opportunities for development.

Staff engagement is a high priority for the NHS as it can improve morale, productivity, organisational performance and patient experience. Research indicates that staff satisfaction – and retention, discretionary effort and productivity – are closely associated with how staff feel about their employer and their sense of engagement with their workplace. The degree of staff involvement in planning and delivering services is an important factor in this, while increasing evidence shows direct links between staff satisfaction and the patient experience.

The NHS Constitution made four pledges to staff:
- to provide all staff with clear roles and responsibilities and rewarding jobs for teams and individuals
- to provide all staff with personal development plans, access to appropriate training and the support of line management to succeed
- to provide support and opportunities for staff to maintain their health, wellbeing and safety
- to engage staff in decisions that affect them and the services they provide individually, through representative organisations and local partnership working arrangements. All staff will be empowered to put forward better ways to deliver better and safer services.

The Constitution places 11 responsibilities on staff. Key ones stipulate that staff should aim to:
- maintain the highest standards of care and service and take responsibility for their contribution to their team and the NHS as a whole
- take up training and development opportunities provided over and above those legally required of their post
- be open with patients and their families, including if anything goes wrong, welcome feedback and address concerns promptly and in a spirit of cooperation.

These responsibilities are not legally binding but enable employers to have clear expectations of staff.

The ninth national NHS staff survey took place from September to December 2011, and asked 250,000 staff about their experiences, with 54 per cent responding. It found high levels of job satisfaction, with 90 per cent feeling they made a difference to patients. Just over half reported working more than their contracted hours. Around half would recommend their trust as a place to work, while 87 per cent were happy with the standard of care. A third were satisfied with the extent to which they felt

Spotlight on policy: Staff health

The Government committed itself to improving NHS staff's health and wellbeing in its public health and *Liberating the NHS* white papers.

The DH commissioned an independent review of the health and wellbeing of NHS staff, led by Dr Steve Boorman, which reported in 2009. This gathered and analysed evidence across the service to better understand the links to productivity, efficiency and patient experience. The review's final report makes 20 recommendations, including:

- NHS organisations should have a prevention-focused health and wellbeing strategy for all staff
- each organisation's senior managers should be made accountable for staff health and wellbeing, measured as part of the annual assessments of NHS performance
- early interventions for staff with musculo-skeletal and mental health conditions to support early return to work.

The review estimated its recommendations could potentially save £555 million and 3.4 million working days – equivalent to 14,900 extra staff. The recommendations were accepted in full and £6.5 million set aside for their implementation.

Two years later, the NHS Future Forum found much of the Boorman report had yet to be fully implemented. It suggested chief executives should report to their boards annually on progress made on improving staff health and wellbeing. The Government accepted all the Forum's recommendations, devised an NHS health and wellbeing improvement framework and announced a 'realignment' of NHS occupational health services.

Further information

NHS health and well-being: final report, DH, November 2009.
NHS health and well-being improvement framework, DH, July 2011.
Healthy staff, better care for patients: realignment of occupational health services to the NHS in England, DH, July 2011.
The NHS's role in the public's health – a report from the NHS Future Forum, NHS Future Forum, January 2012.

their trust valued their work, but many felt excluded from decision-making, with only 30 per cent saying senior managers acted on their feedback. Eight per cent reported experiencing physical violence from patients, their relatives or other members of the public, while just under a third reported work-related stress.

Further information

National NHS Staff Survey Co-ordination Centre **www.nhsstaffsurveys.com**
Briefing 79: Staff engagement in the NHS: some local experience, NHS Employers, November 2010.
www.nhsemployers.org/staffengagement

09 Evidence, research and development

Policy for health and healthcare must be based on reliable evidence about the population's needs and what will work best to meet them. Such evidence originates from many types of research, covering prevention of ill health, promotion of health, disease management, patient care, delivery of healthcare and its organisation, as well as public health and social care. Conducting research to improve health and medical treatments was one of the NHS's founding principles, and the UK health research system has an even longer tradition of excellence: the Medical Research Council has funded 29 Nobel prize-winners since it was founded in 1913. This reputation, combined with the existence of a national health service, attracts high levels of research and development (R&D) investment from the pharmaceutical and biotechnology industries – an important part of the UK 'knowledge economy'.

The Government reaffirmed the importance of research in its *Liberating the NHS* white paper, stating: 'The Government is committed to the promotion and conduct of research as a core NHS role'. In the 2010 spending review it promised to 'increase spending on health research in real terms', while the 2011 *Plan for growth* highlighted the key role of health research in the national economy.

The ambition is for the NHS to foster a culture that pioneers new treatments so it becomes a hive of research activity attracting the best researchers in the world.

Government, strategy and infrastructure

Department of Health's role
The DH invests in research to support government objectives for public health, health services and social care, as well as contributing to the government science strategy. To deliver these objectives, the DH:
• identifies needs and priorities for R&D in health and social care
• persuades other organisations to fund R&D that falls within their remits
• provides support funding for non-commercial research in NHS organisations
• funds and manages R&D not picked up by others
• supports synthesis of research and dissemination of findings to users
• uses research in policy-making
• contributes to wider government science and technology strategy.

The DH keeps its research priorities under review. They are decided through discussion with policy colleagues and ministers. In the NHS, priorities are identified through consultation with clinicians, managers and patients. They take account of the burden of disease, potential benefits and DH objectives, as well as the responsibilities and work of other funders, including charities.

Supporting and promoting R&D will remain a core function of the DH after the NHS reorganisation. The NHS Commissioning Board will also 'promote involvement in research and the use of research evidence'.

National Institute for Health Research

The aim of the National Institute for Health Research (NIHR) is to create a health research system in which the NHS supports outstanding individuals working in world-class facilities and conducting leading-edge research focused on the needs of patients and the public. NIHR:

- supports individuals carrying out and participating in research
- commissions and funds research
- provides facilities for a thriving research environment
- creates unified, streamlined and simple knowledge-management systems.

Its programmes are:

- applied research – grants for leading researchers with an impressive track-record; the first were made in mental health, medicines for children, diabetes, stroke and dementias, neuro-degenerative diseases and neurology
- research for patient benefit (RfPB) – addresses issues of importance to the NHS, including research into everyday practice
- invention for innovation research (i4i) – aims to support and advance the development of innovative medical technologies
- public health research (PHR) – on the benefits, costs, acceptability and wider effect of non-NHS interventions such as prevention of obesity in children and speed humps for preventing road accidents
- health services and delivery research (HS&DR) – intended to produce evidence on the quality, access and organisation of health services, including costs and outcomes
- healthcare technology cooperatives (HTCs) – funding for NHS organisations to act as centres of expertise to develop new concepts, demonstrate proof of principle and devise research protocols for new medical devices, healthcare technologies or technology-dependent interventions

- health technology assessment (HTA) – to ensure healthcare professionals, NHS managers, the public and patients have the latest information on the costs, effectiveness and impact of health technology developments
- efficacy and mechanism evaluation (EME) – includes clinical trials and evaluative studies with an expectation of substantial health gain
- NHS physical environment research and development – improving the way property and facilities are managed and maintained, and promoting safe, high-quality and best-value design.

NIHR supports national research schools that bring together academics and practitioners. The School for Primary Care is a partnership of five academic centres and focuses on research to improve everyday practice in primary care. The School for Social Care Research, a partnership between six academic centres, aims to enhance the evidence base for adult social care practice. The establishment of the School of Public Health Research was announced in 2011.

NIHR's clinical research networks support clinical trials throughout England, and promote patient and public involvement in health research. They have increased numbers taking part in clinical trials, and improved their speed, quality and coordination. The UK now has the highest national per capita rate of cancer trial participation in the world. There are six topic-specific networks for cancer, dementia and neuro-degenerative diseases, diabetes, medicines for children, mental health and stroke. Another covers primary care. NIHR has also set up a comprehensive NHS research network covering all other diseases and areas of need.

Its biomedical research centres and units, and its nine collaborations for leadership in applied health research and care (see page 196) are partnerships designed to ensure the results of research make a timely impact on patient outcomes.

NIHR's annual budget incorporates all previously existing funds for NHS research in England, as well as NHS funding that supports clinical research and academics.
www.nihr.ac.uk

Health Research Authority
The Government's *Liberating the NHS … next steps* white paper noted that several bodies had responsibility for research regulation, and announced

NHS Evidence

NHS Evidence is a web portal providing access to authoritative clinical and non-clinical evidence and best practice. Launched in 2009 and managed by NICE, NHS Evidence aims to be a 'one-stop shop' for health information for the NHS in England. Drawing on local, national and international sources, it covers primary research, summarised clinical evidence, policy documents, commissioning and drugs. Information from the British National Formulary is a key element. It awards an accreditation mark to organisations that meet high standards in developing health information. Through 'My Evidence' users can personalise a search and register to receive the latest information. NHS Evidence is designed for professionals but is accessible to the public, and is intended to be as easy to use as any internet search engine.
www.evidence.nhs.uk

UK Clinical Trials Gateway

The UK Clinical Trials Gateway enables patients and their clinicians to locate and contact trials of interest to them. The information is taken from a variety of national registers that are publicly available. The UKCTG is run by NIHR on behalf of all the UK health departments, and involves clinical research charities, research professionals and patient representatives.
www.ukctg.nihr.ac.uk

plans to rationalise arrangements. The purpose of the new Health Research Authority (HRA), launched in December 2011, is to streamline regulation by reducing duplication of R&D checks and improve the cost-effectiveness of clinical trials. It promises to promote consistent, proportionate standards for compliance and inspection.

In its initial form as a special health authority, the HRA has the National Research Ethics Service as its core. Work is underway on establishing the HRA as a non-departmental public body, which will enable it to take on more functions: eventually it will take over the Secretary of State's role of approving the processing of patient information for medical research. Consultation will be held on the future of the Human Fertilisation and Embryology Authority to decide if its research-related functions should pass to the HRA.
www.nres.nhs.uk/hra

Office for Strategic Co-ordination of Health Research (OSCHR)

OSCHR was established as a government office to work with the Medical Research Council (MRC) and NIHR on developing a single integrated strategy covering all areas of health research. Key functions are to:

- work with officials to set the Government's health research strategy, taking into account advice on priorities and needs from NIHR, its equivalents in Scotland, Wales and Northern Ireland, the MRC and the NHS
- set a budget for the strategy and submit a single bid to the Treasury
- communicate the UK's health priorities to the pharmaceutical and bioscience sectors
- monitor delivery of the strategy against objectives and report to Parliament on progress
- encourage a stronger partnership between Government, health industries and charities.

Further information

A shared vision for UK health research, OSCHR, March 2010.

Office for Life Sciences

The Office for Life Sciences (OLS) was established in 2009 in recognition that more needed to be done to support a thriving UK environment for the life sciences: pharmaceuticals, medical technology and medical biotechnology. Life sciences are seen as one of the high-tech strategic industries important in driving growth and prosperity, continuing improvements in healthcare and meeting future challenges such as an ageing population and obesity. OLS has four priorities:

- strengthening the NHS as an innovation champion
- building a more integrated life sciences industry
- ensuring access to finance and stimulating investment
- marketing the UK life sciences industry overseas.

The Government's life sciences strategy is based on three aims:

- building a life sciences 'ecosystem' – making it easier for researchers to commercialise academic research, placing clinical research at the heart of the NHS and enabling patients to participate in research
- attracting, developing and rewarding talent – offering careers for clinicians, scientists and technicians from around the world
- overcoming barriers and creating incentives for promoting healthcare innovation – encouraging early-stage investment and bridging funding gaps to secure follow-on investment.

Milestones in NHS research

During its 64-year history, the NHS has played a central role in health R&D. Major discoveries involving the NHS include:

- in 1950, Sir Richard Doll and Sir Austin Bradford Hill discovered a link between smoking and lung cancer; in 1954, 80 per cent of UK adults smoked – now only 21 per cent do
- in 1962, orthopaedic surgeon Sir John Charnley was the first to perform a total hip replacement, at Wrightington Hospital, Wigan; the NHS now carries out more than 62,000 hip replacements a year
- in 1978, the world's first IVF baby, Louise Brown, was born in Oldham General Hospital; more than 1 million 'test tube babies' have been born since
- in the 1990s, Professor Lesley Regan of St Mary's Hospital, London, discovered that 15 per cent of women who suffered recurrent miscarriages carried antibodies in their blood that made it prone to clotting; she found that by treating such women with aspirin and heparin their rate of live births rose from 10 to 70 per cent.

Further information

60 years of research in the NHS benefiting patients, NIHR, June 2008.

Further information

Strategy for UK life sciences, OLS/Department for Business, Innovation and Skills, December 2011.
Investing in UK health and life sciences, HM Government, December 2011.
www.bis.gov.uk/ols

Funding R&D

Who funds R&D?

Each year the Government and healthcare charities spend over £2 billion on healthcare research. The DH is the largest single public sector contributor, but it is not the only funder of UK health and social care research. The funding councils, research councils – especially the MRC – and research charities all play significant roles. Industry is a major investor in healthcare R&D. The health departments in Scotland, Wales and Northern Ireland also support health and social care R&D. Other government departments provide research funding too.

Spending review funding

After the 2010 spending review (see page 106) the DH announced that through its policy research programme and NIHR it would increase spending on health research in real terms up to 2015. The Government also announced that the MRC's budget would be maintained in real terms.

Programme grants for applied research

A key strand of the R&D strategy is to support applied health research addressing the NHS's priorities and needs. NIHR's programme grants for applied research make available funding up to £2 million over three to five years from the scheme's annual budget of £38 million. The aim is to:

- provide evidence to improve health outcomes through promoting health, preventing ill health, and disease management, particularly for conditions causing significant disease burden, where other research funders may not be focused or insufficient funding is available
- enable NHS trusts to tackle areas of high priority or need for health improvement
- provide stable funding to support long-term development of top-quality applied research groups in the NHS.

Research organisations

Apart from the main statutory bodies, other organisations play an important part in gathering and analysing evidence and promoting R&D.

UK Cochrane Centre

The UKCC was established in 1992 to facilitate and coordinate systematic reviews of randomised controlled trials. It is now part of NIHR and one of 14 Cochrane Centres around the world which provide the infrastructure for coordinating the Cochrane Collaboration, an international, not-for-profit, independent organisation, dedicated to making up-to-date, accurate information about the effects of healthcare readily available worldwide. The Cochrane Library is a regularly updated collection of evidence-based medicine databases, including the Cochrane database of systematic reviews, which provides high-quality information to professionals and the public.

UK Cochrane Centre http://ukcc.cochrane.org
Cochrane Collaboration www.cochrane.org

UK Clinical Research Collaboration

The UK Clinical Research Collaboration, established in 2004, brings together the NHS, research funders, industry, regulatory bodies, Royal Colleges, patient groups and academe to promote high-quality clinical research. Its main activities are:

- developing a comprehensive infrastructure to underpin clinical research
- building an expert research workforce to support clinical research
- developing incentives for research in the NHS
- streamlining regulations and governance
- developing a coordinated approach to research funding.

www.ukcrc.org

Health Services Research Network

HSRN is a membership network that connects NHS organisations, universities, research institutes, commercial and professional organisations, and third sector bodies that support research into the financing, organisation, planning and delivery of health services. It seeks to influence policy-makers and managers to support better use of research, campaigns for secure funding for health services research and for measures to improve the careers of those engaged in it. It also supports senior, middle and new NHS managers in driving innovation and implementing best practice. HSRN helps them access and understand the latest health services research, enabling them to work with their peers, leading academics and service leaders from other sectors on how best to use research knowledge to improve the services they manage.

www.nhsconfed.org/HSRN

Nurturing innovation

Innovation now has a higher profile role than ever in the NHS: it is vital to improving outcomes for patients and helping achieve the major savings required by the QIPP challenge (see page 170). Rapidly spreading changes that improve quality and productivity to all parts of the NHS has become an urgent priority.

Innovation under review

The UK is slow in adopting innovative practice compared with other developed economies. It took five years before half the adult patients admitted to NHS acute care received a venous thrombo-embolism risk assessment, despite a death rate estimated at 24,000 people every year. When it was made a national clinical priority, risk assessment became routine for 84 per cent of admissions within a year. Despite pioneering work on MRI scanners, it has only 500 out of 20,000 worldwide, performing less than 2 per cent of the world's 60 million scans each year, at only two-thirds of the international average use per machine.

In 2011, the NHS chief executive's innovation review identified six barriers to the diffusion of innovative ideas in the NHS:
• poor access to evidence, data and metrics
• insufficient recognition and celebration of innovation and innovators
• financial levers that do not reward innovators and can discourage diffusion
• commissioners lacking the tools or capability to drive innovation
• leadership culture to support innovation inconsistent or lacking
• lack of effective or systematic architecture.

It recommended:
• reducing variation and driving greater compliance with NICE guidance
• developing better innovation uptake metrics and more accessible evidence and information about new ideas
• building cross-boundary networks for more systematic diffusion and collaboration
• aligning organisational, financial and personal incentives and investment to reward innovation
• improving procurement arrangements
• 'hard wiring' innovation into training and education for managers and clinicians
• strengthening leadership, setting clearer priorities and sharpening local accountability for innovation
• identifying and mandating adoption of high-impact innovations.

Further information
Briefing 207: Being a good research partner: the virtues and rewards, NHS Confederation/ SDO Network, October 2010.
Innovation, health and wealth: accelerating adoption and diffusion in the NHS, DH, December 2011.

The innovation landscape
A wide range of NHS organisations are taking a lead in encouraging innovation.

CLAHRCs
NIHR's nine collaborations for leadership in applied health research and care (CLAHRCs) are partnerships between a university and the surrounding NHS organisations, focused on improving patient outcomes by applying health research. They began work in 2008, promoting approaches to research that are designed to take account of how healthcare is now delivered across sectors and wide geographical areas. CLAHRCs also aim to build NHS capacity for evidence-informed change in

local services. NIHR provides core funding – typically £5 million to £10 million over five years – which CLAHRCs must match.

Biomedical research centres and units

NIHR is investing £775 million over five years in biomedical research centres and units investigating major causes of illness and death such as cancer, heart disease, asthma, HIV, mental illness, blindness, childhood diseases and ageing. The 12 centres are partnerships between the NHS and universities in London, Oxford, Cambridge, Manchester, Liverpool and Newcastle. They are complemented by 16 biomedical research units taking advances in medical research into the hospital. Their work focuses on areas traditionally receiving limited research funding, including gastrointestinal and liver disease, deafness, musculo-skeletal disease and nutrition.

Academic health science centres

Five partnerships between research, education and health service bodies were designated as academic health science centres (AHSCs) in 2009, chosen by an international peer review panel. They will benefit mainly from recognition and prestige rather than extra funding, enabling them to compete with internationally renowned centres such as Harvard and Johns Hopkins in the USA and Sweden's Karolinska Institute. AHSC status is awarded for five years, when designation will be subject to review and re-application.

Academic health science networks

The Government plans to establish academic health science networks during 2012/13. These will support AHSCs and build on their models of accelerating adoption and diffusion, aligning education, clinical research, informatics, innovation, training and education, and healthcare delivery. Working with AHSCs, they will identify high-impact innovations and spread their use at pace and scale throughout their networks. They will work with industry to scope problems and jointly develop solutions to key health challenges. The DH hopes every NHS organisation will aspire to be affiliated to its local AHSN.

Health innovation and education clusters

The 17 HIECs announced at the end of 2009 are collaborations across primary, community and secondary care, universities and colleges, and industry. They provide professional education and training and promote innovation in healthcare by speeding up the adoption of research.

NHS Technology Adoption Centre

Based in Manchester and launched in 2007, NTAC's mission is to increase the NHS's uptake of new technology, identify technologies that will improve healthcare and promote greater cooperation between organisations developing and using healthcare technologies. It works at a clinical, managerial and procurement level, scanning the medical technology industry for innovations and organising regular calls for innovative products. If NTAC is aware that increased uptake of a technology would benefit the NHS, it carries out a technology adoption review to identify barriers to adoption.

www.technologyadoptioncentre.nhs.uk

NHS National Innovation Centre

NIC aims to speed up development of pre-commercial technologies likely to benefit the NHS. It provides free online tools to help assess ideas and find resources. It can link with national and international organisations to tailor-make plans for rapidly developing intellectual property. NIC also issues to industry and academe 'calls for solutions' to meet particular NHS needs.

www.nic.nhs.uk

Innovation hubs

NIC coordinates eight regional innovation hubs set up between 2002 and 2005, which support entrepreneurial activity by helping trusts identify and commercialise their innovations, protecting intellectual property and seeking appropriate partners so the NHS can benefit financially from its own inventions.

www.innovations.nhs.uk

10 Information technology

A modern IT infrastructure is vital to improving patient safety and enabling choice, helping clinicians to work efficiently and allowing them access to patient information promptly and securely. The health and social care systems must use and communicate information effectively to maintain and improve the quality of care and their ability to manage demand in tight financial conditions.

IT policy and the information strategy

The end of NPfIT
The previous Labour Government made major investments in NHS IT, devising in 2002 an ambitious £12 billion national programme to install systems throughout the service. But the National Programme for IT (NPfIT) attracted widespread criticism that it was too centralised, too expensive and constantly behind schedule.

Under the coalition Government, a DH review of NPfIT concluded that a centralised, national approach was no longer required, and that a more locally led plural system of procurement should supersede it while continuing with national applications already procured. The DH characterised this approach as 'connect all' rather than 'replace all' systems. By the time NPfIT was dismantled, it had cost £6.4 billion.

However, the national infrastructure has been preserved, as applications such as Choose and Book and the Electronic Prescription Service (see page 204) have now been integrated into the NHS. These are no longer managed as projects but as IT services under the NHS's control. Organisations can use and develop the IT they already have and add to it by integrating systems bought either through existing national contracts or elsewhere.

The DH and Intellect, the technology trade association, are exploring ways to stimulate the healthcare IT marketplace and encourage small and medium-sized companies excluded under NPfIT.

Further information
A joint plan to foster a healthy and vibrant healthcare IT market: initial issue, Intellect/DH informatics directorate, January 2012.

Devising an information strategy

The Government proposed in 2010 an 'information revolution' as part of its *Liberating the NHS* reorganisation. It identified the key issues as:

- ensuring basic data meets necessary standards
- using the NHS number (see page 205) as a unique identifier
- 'interoperability' – allowing information to move freely and meaningfully through the system.

The Government undertook to develop, following consultation, an information strategy that would 'define the vision, set the expectations, describe the responsibilities, provide the timetable, and determine the routes' by which the information revolution would be achieved. This is now expected during 2012. In addition, the Chancellor's 2011 Autumn Statement contained the promise that all NHS patients would be able to access their GP records online by 2015.

The NHS Future Forum concluded that barriers to more effective use of information were 'more cultural than technological. What is needed more than anything is a change of mindset in the NHS'. Despite a decade of IT investment, the Forum found: 'The widespread inability of the NHS to communicate electronically and its reliance on "snail mail" is a cause of much frustration, at sharp odds with practice in almost every other walk of life, and is increasingly a matter of reputational risk for the NHS.' Delay in publishing the information strategy had 'reduced momentum for change and created a climate of uncertainty and drift'. It warned that the NHS could not remain in the 'information dark ages', and called for:

- universal adoption of the NHS number across health and social care by 2013
- presumption in favour of hospital discharge summaries being made available to the GP and patient at the point of discharge, and for GP referral letters to be made available at the point of referral
- a review of information governance rules during 2012
- contracts to require all NHS or social care providers to share their data electronically
- a clear deadline in the current Parliament for putting all information on clinical outcomes into the public domain
- each NHS organisation to appoint a clinician responsible for organising information to support better care.

Key organisation: NHS Connecting for Health

NHS Connecting for Health (CFH) is part of the DH's informatics directorate, and was set up in 2005. Its role is to maintain and develop the NHS national IT infrastructure, which includes a number of national services and a range of national applications. Staff are drawn from across the NHS, civil service, academe and the private sector, and encompass management, IT, clinical and medical skills. CFH offers advice on systems installed across the NHS and on IT suppliers.
www.connectingforhealth.nhs.uk

The Government promised the Forum's recommendations would be taken forward in the information strategy.

Further information

Liberating the NHS: an information revolution – a consultation on proposals, DH, October 2010.
Autumn Statement 2011, HM Treasury, November 2011.
Information – a report from the NHS Future Forum, NHS Future Forum, January 2012.

IT infrastructure

The NHS national IT infrastructure includes:
• summary care records
• GP2GP
• Choose and Book, the electronic booking service for hospital appointments
• Electronic Prescription Service (EPS)
• picture archiving and communications systems (PACS)
• N3: a national broadband IT network
• NHSmail, a central email and directory service for the NHS
• NHS Choices
• HealthSpace
• NHSweb.

Summary care record

Historically, little or no information has been available to clinical staff when patients are seen out-of-hours or in an emergency. One of NPfIT's aims was to create a fully integrated system in which every patient had an individual electronic care record that could be rapidly transmitted between different parts of the NHS and made available to staff at all times. This has proved beyond the DH's capacity and it is no longer seeking a universal system.

Instead patients will have a summary care record (SCR) that will contain essential health information about any medicines, allergies and adverse reactions derived from their GP record. Once SCRs are created, they will be available to authorised NHS staff who need access to the information in urgent and emergency care. Patients will be able to access their SCR using the HealthSpace website (see page 205).

By early 2012, almost 11 million SCRs had been created, 35 million patients contacted and 1,598 GP practices had loaded records to the SCR. Patients may choose not to have a record created or not to have it shared, but only 1.24 per cent have so far opted out.

Further information
The care record guarantee: our guarantee for NHS care records in England – version 5, National Information Governance Board for Health and Social Care, January 2011. *The National Programme for IT: an update on the delivery of detailed care records systems: forty-fifth report of session 2010–12,* House of Commons public accounts committee, July 2011.
www.nhscarerecords.nhs.uk
www.nigb.nhs.uk

GP2GP
The GP2GP project enables the electronic transfer of patients' healthcare records from one GP surgery to another. It is designed to ensure records are available to the new GP within 24 hours of a patient registering with their practice. By late 2011, 56 per cent of practices in England were using GP2GP and had made 1.9 million transfers.

Choose and Book
Choose and Book, the electronic booking service, is designed to underpin the policy of enabling patients to choose which hospital to attend at a date and time to suit them. The software allows GPs and other primary care staff to make initial hospital or clinic outpatient appointments before the patient has left the surgery. This enables clinicians to track referrals more easily and conduct email discussion about cases when necessary. It also provides more consistent, accurate and efficient referral information without the delays of paper correspondence. Choose and Book should reduce the chance of patients not turning up for appointments and improve clinical governance by providing an audit trail.
www.chooseandbook.nhs.uk

Electronic Prescription Service

The Electronic Prescription Service (EPS) enables prescriptions to be transferred electronically to a pharmacist nominated by the patient. Electronic transmission increases patient safety by reducing prescription errors and providing better information at the point of prescribing and dispensing. This creates the opportunity to reduce adverse drug events where the patient responds poorly to medication. Over 623 million prescription messages had been transmitted electronically by January 2012. Over 8,000 GP practices and 9,000 pharmacies were using EPS.

PACS

Picture archiving and communications systems (PACS) were a great success for NPfIT and are now being used in every hospital trust in England. They use digital imaging technology to store x-rays and scans electronically, enabling them to be viewed on screens instantly and simultaneously at multiple locations. The current supplier contracts for PACS end in 2013 and 2014: extensions are being negotiated. The national PACS programme is helping manage the transition of these systems to local ownership.

N3: the New National Network

N3 provides the entire NHS with fast broadband networking services, and forms the essential technical infrastructure for other major projects. It replaced the earlier NHSnet, saving £900 million over seven years, and is one of the world's largest virtual private networks. Clinicians can send high-quality images to specialists for remote diagnosis and use N3 for secure clinical messaging. It makes video conferencing and remote working easier, and saves on telephone costs by enabling NHS organisations to converge their voice and data networks. It is intended to be flexible enough for future needs and allow the NHS to take early advantage of improvements in technology. Connections to N3 started in 2004. About 1.3 million NHS employees have access, including all GP practices.
www.n3.nhs.uk

NHSmail

NHSmail is a secure national email and directory service for NHS staff in England and Scotland, developed specifically to meet the British Medical Association's requirements for clinical email between NHS organisations. It provides a national directory of people in the NHS, containing the name, email addresses, telephone numbers, name and address of their organisation, and information about departments, job roles and specialties. Staff are assigned an email address that moves with them if they change job or location within the NHS.

NHS Choices

NHS Choices is the NHS's online service for the public, providing information on 750 health conditions and treatments, healthy living and health and social care services. It provides a 'front door' for the public to all NHS online services and information through the country's biggest health website. This includes information to help people find services and compare hospitals. NHS Choices receives 10 million visits a month.
www.nhs.uk

HealthSpace

HealthSpace is a secure website where patients can store personal health information online, such as height, weight and blood pressure. It is free and available for all NHS patients living in England aged 16 and over. Anyone living in an area that has adopted the summary care record system can view their SCR through an Advanced HealthSpace account. HealthSpace Communicator allows patient-to-clinician messaging in some areas.
www.healthspace.nhs.uk

NHS number

The NHS number is the common currency of NHS information. Babies born in England and Wales are allocated an NHS number at birth. It is a unique identifier that provides a common link between a patient's records – electronic and manual – across the NHS. It consists of ten digits: the first nine are the identifier and the tenth is a check digit used to confirm the number's validity. It is the cornerstone of the move towards a summary care record, and enables disparate information to be collated into a comprehensive record of a person's health. The NHS Future Forum has said that universal adoption of the NHS number across health and social care 'must be turned from a long-held – and generally ignored – aspiration into a reality by 2013'.

Collecting and using data

Collecting data from frontline NHS organisations is necessary to ensure patient safety and provide accountability. But for some time it has been apparent that the burden of data collection continues to grow disproportionately, with much duplication and overlap to satisfy the demands of inspection and regulatory bodies. The DH has therefore introduced a policy of collecting only essential data, designed to ensure that:
• collections fit with national policies
• requests for the same information are not repeated
• NHS organisations can complete requests for data in as little time as possible.

The Information Centre's Review of Central Returns (ROCR) process aims to minimise central data demands on the NHS from the DH and its arm's-length bodies. It regularly reviews all information requirements and approves requests for information – including one-off surveys – taking account of the NHS effort involved in supplying the data requested. Only collections that have been through this process are added to the list of authorised central returns. If a request does not contain an ROCR number, NHS staff do not need to complete it. Even the need for data to answer parliamentary questions or support public expenditure survey negotiations is not a justification in itself for ROCR support.

The DH has developed UNIFY to act as a single 'warehouse' for information previously recorded on several local systems to meet different reporting requirements. Once data is captured, it now needs to be input only once. This frees the NHS from multiple requests for additional information.

The Government made a commitment in the *Liberating the NHS* white paper to 'initiate a fundamental review of data returns, with the aim of culling returns of limited value'. The review subsequently identified a total of 305 data collections, of which 197 were commissioned by the DH and 108 by arm's-length bodies. The review's recommendations were then put out to consultation. If accepted, they would result in 25 per cent of returns being discontinued.

Further information
Fundamental review of data returns: a consultation on the recommendations of the review, DH, August 2011.
UNIFY www.unify2.dh.nhs.uk/unify

Key organisation **Information Centre for Health and Social Care**
The Information Centre for Health and Social Care is a special health authority that collects data from across health and social care, analyses it and converts it into useful information. Set up in 2005, it aims to improve information quality and data standards, improve access to information and deliver the information that frontline services need, as well as being the source of data for official statistics. It provides data to support commissioning and clinical audit, together with statistics on the NHS workforce, finance and performance, public health and social care. The Health and Social Care Act enhanced the Centre's powers over information collection across all organisations in the health and social care system.
www.ic.nhs.uk

11 The NHS in Scotland

While variations in the NHS's structure and policy emphasis have always existed in different parts of the UK, they have become more prominent since devolution, especially in Scotland. The NHS in Scotland has abolished the structure which was a legacy of the internal market of the 1990s, replacing it with an integrated system that stresses collaboration and cooperation between organisations rather than competition.

The structure of NHSScotland

Ultimate responsibility for the NHS in Scotland lies no longer with Westminster but with the Scottish Parliament, and specifically the Scottish Government's cabinet secretary for health, wellbeing and cities strategy. The Scottish Government Health and Social Care Directorates have strategic responsibility for the service. A range of special health boards provide services nationally, while locally 14 NHS boards both plan and provide services. Community health partnerships manage primary and community health services.

The Scottish Parliament

The Scottish Parliament at Holyrood opened in 1999 with powers devolved from the UK Parliament covering matters that include health, social work, education, housing and local government. Its 129 members (MSPs) can therefore pass primary and secondary legislation affecting Scotland on a range of domestic issues. Issues concerning Scotland that have a UK or international impact are dealt with by the UK Parliament in Westminster. These 'reserved matters' include foreign affairs and defence, but also certain health-related issues:
• professional regulation
• abortion
• human fertilisation
• genetics
• control and safety of medicines.

The UK Parliament can also make laws that will apply to Scotland on any subject, but does not normally legislate on devolved matters without the consent of the Scottish Parliament.

Committees play a central part in the Parliament's work, taking evidence from witnesses, scrutinising legislation and conducting inquiries. The health and sport committee considers health policy and NHSScotland, plus matters such as community care, public health and food safety, as well as sport. It is responsible for considering any proposed legislation that falls within its remit. This includes legislation setting out the Scottish Government's budget proposals for each financial year. The committee also commissions research, conducts inquiries and considers petitions submitted by the public. It has nine members, assigned between the parties on a proportional basis.

In addition, some of the Parliament's seven mandatory committees take an interest in NHSScotland: for example, the finance committee is concerned with public expenditure and how the Scottish Government's budget is spent, while the public audit committee holds NHS boards to account for how they spend taxpayers' money and ensures public funds are spent effectively.

The Scotland Office, led by the Secretary of State for Scotland, represents Scottish interests in the UK Government and Parliament and manages day-to-day devolution issues from the Westminster perspective. There are 59 MPs at Westminster representing Scottish constituencies.
www.scottish.parliament.uk
www.scotlandoffice.gov.uk

The Scottish Government
The devolved Scottish Government's relationship with the Scottish Parliament is similar to the relationship between the UK Government and the UK Parliament at Westminster. Members of the Scottish Government are chosen from the party or parties holding the largest number of seats in the Parliament.

The Scottish Government is led by a First Minister, elected by the Scottish Parliament, who appoints an eight-strong cabinet of Scottish ministers. Although the civil service in Scotland remains part of the home civil service, civil servants there are accountable to Scottish ministers, who are themselves accountable to the Scottish Parliament. The Scottish Government administers an annual budget of over £30 billion.
www.scotland.gov.uk

Scottish Government Health and Social Care Directorates
The Scottish Government Health and Social Care Directorates are responsible for NHSScotland as well as for developing and implementing health and community care policy. These directorates cover:
• health finance and information
• health workforce and performance
• health and healthcare improvement

- chief nursing officer, patients, public and health professions
- chief medical officer – public health and sport
- health and social care integration
- children and families.

They provide the statutory and financial framework for NHSScotland and hold it to account for its performance. The Scottish Government has discretion to intervene if serious problems arise locally.

Health, Wellbeing and Cities has three ministers: the cabinet secretary for health, wellbeing and cities strategy, the minister for public health and the minister for Commonwealth Games and sport. The director general – health and social care is the chief executive of NHSScotland, and is accountable to ministers for its efficiency and performance.

Scotland's chief medical officer (CMO) is the Scottish Government's principal medical adviser, with direct access to ministers. The post has direct involvement in developing health policy, including prevention, health promotion, health protection and harm reduction. The CMO has lead responsibility for issues such as clinical effectiveness, quality assurance, accreditation and research, and covers the spectrum of health-related issues ranging from public health policy to NHS operations.

Further information
NHSScotland chief executive's annual report 2010/11, Scottish Government, November 2011.

Special health boards
Eight special health boards provide services nationally. They account for about £1.09 billion of the total NHSScotland budget of £11.6 billion in 2012/13. They are:

National Waiting Times Centre, comprising the Golden Jubilee National Hospital and the Beardmore Hotel and Conference Centre, both in Clydebank near Glasgow and bought from the private sector in 2002. The hospital carries out only elective procedures in key specialties to reduce waiting times. The NHS-owned four-star Beardmore Hotel has 168 bedrooms and a 170-seat auditorium, and is a national NHS and public sector conference facility.
www.nhsgoldenjubilee.co.uk
www.thebeardmore.com

NHS 24, which provides 24-hour telephone access (0845 242424) to medical advice from clinical professionals and acts as a referral point to local out-of-hours services. It takes 1.5 million calls a year. It also runs NHS inform, a health advice service offering information on medical conditions by phone (0800 224488) and a website.
www.nhs24.com
www.nhsinform.co.uk

NHS Education for Scotland, which designs, commissions and provides education, training and development for NHSScotland's workforce.
www.nes.scot.nhs.uk

NHS Health Scotland, whose work involves tackling inequalities and all aspects of health improvement, from gathering evidence, to planning, delivery and evaluation.
www.healthscotland.com

Healthcare Improvement Scotland, which was formed in 2011. HIS's role is to scrutinise the quality and safety of care provided by NHSScotland and the independent sector, as well as identify evidence for improvement. Its Scottish Health Technologies Group (SHTG) advises on evidence about the clinical and cost-effectiveness of existing and new technologies. HIS is also responsible for the Scottish Intercollegiate Guidelines Network (SIGN), which develops evidence-based clinical practice guidelines.
www.healthcareimprovementscotland.org
www.sign.ac.uk

Scottish Ambulance Service, which employs over 4,300 staff who responded to 650,000 emergencies and carried out 3,700 air ambulance missions in 2010/11.
www.scottishambulance.com

State Hospitals Board for Scotland, which serves both Scotland and Northern Ireland and provides 140 beds for male mentally ill patients needing treatment under secure conditions at Carstairs.
www.tsh.scot.nhs.uk

National Services Scotland, which provides specialist legal services, counter-fraud services, health statistics, screening programmes, family health service payments and patient registration. It also monitors clinical standards, as well as overseeing Health Facilities Scotland, the Scottish National Blood Transfusion Service and Health Protection Scotland, which

carries out surveillance of communicable diseases, environmental health
hazards and public health.
www.nhsnss.org

NHS boards

NHSScotland abolished trusts in 2004 in favour of local single-system
working based on 14 (originally 15) NHS boards (11 mainland and three
island boards). This was intended to instil shared aims, common values
and clear lines of accountability while breaking down traditional barriers
between primary and acute care.

Scottish NHS board areas

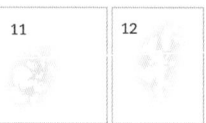

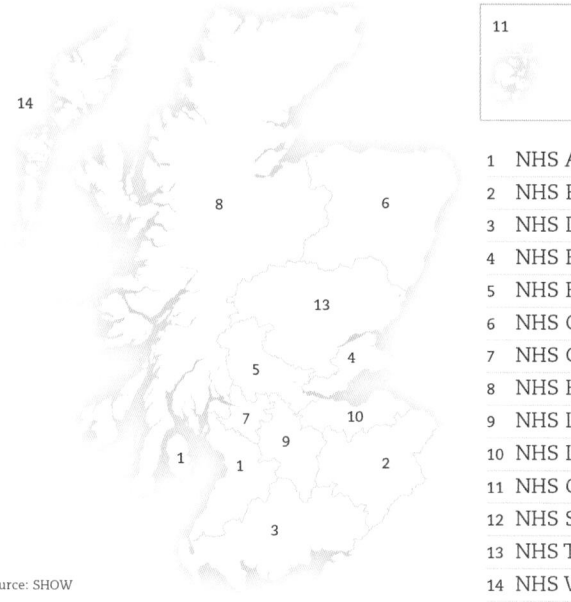

Source: SHOW

1 NHS Ayrshire and Arran
2 NHS Borders
3 NHS Dumfries and Galloway
4 NHS Fife
5 NHS Forth Valley
6 NHS Grampian
7 NHS Greater Glasgow
8 NHS Highland
9 NHS Lanarkshire
10 NHS Lothian
11 NHS Orkney
12 NHS Shetland
13 NHS Tayside
14 NHS Western Isles

NHS boards are mainly responsible for:
- protecting and improving their population's health
- delivering hospital, community and primary care services
- developing a local health plan to address health priorities and needs
- allocating resources according to the board's strategic objectives
- performance management of the local health system.

Spotlight on policy: elected NHS boards

After the Scottish Parliament unanimously passed the Health Boards (Membership and Elections) Bill in March 2009, NHS Fife and NHS Dumfries and Galloway piloted the first ever direct elections to health boards, in June 2010.

Directly elected members and elected councillors now form a majority of members on the two boards, with the elected members replacing some of those previously appointed by ministers. They receive the same level of remuneration as appointed members, currently around £7,500 per year.

The elections used the single transferable vote system, and were carried out as all-postal ballots. For the first time in any UK election, 16- and 17-year-olds had the right to stand and vote. In Fife 60 candidates stood and 12 were elected on a turnout of 14 per cent, while 70 took part in Dumfries and Galloway and ten were elected on a 22 per cent turnout. Since the elections some of the original elected members have stepped down from their positions.

The pilots will run for at least two years, and an independent evaluation is expected to report in autumn 2012, after which the Scottish Parliament will decide whether to extend the policy. The pilots cost £2.86 million, funded from central Scottish Government budgets.

Fife and Dumfries and Galloway were chosen to ensure the pilots could test the full range of issues likely to be encountered by a health board in both predominantly urban and rural settings. NHS Lothian and NHS Grampian ran two non-statutory pilots to test ways to improve the range of applicants for board membership.

The policy intention behind the Health Boards (Membership and Elections) Act is to improve public engagement and increase trust in decision-making processes by strengthening the NHS's local democratic accountability.

Boards have a statutory duty to take part in regional and national planning as part of regional planning groups. Since 2008 the three island health boards – Western Isles, Orkney and Shetland – have been strengthened through partnerships with mainland boards designed to allow the larger organisations to use their wider range of resources to support the island boards. For example, Orkney has partnered Grampian, which provides support in public health, healthcare-associated infections, financial analysis support, human resources and delivery of Orkney's clinical services strategy.

Board members are appointed by Scottish ministers, although appointments of non-executives are overseen by the Office of the Commissioner for Public Appointments in Scotland. Members divide into three categories:
• non-executive lay members, including the board chair
• non-executive 'stakeholder' members
• executive members.

Boards have between five and nine non-executive lay members. The chair, who is appointed directly by ministers – not elected by board members – is always a non-executive lay person. Each NHS board includes, as full non-executive directors:
• an employee director
• the chair of the area clinical forum
• the chair of the community health partnership advisory forum
• a representative from the university medical school (where applicable)
• an elected council member from each local authority area covered by the board.

There is no limit to the number of members per board, and overall size and balance varies. The largest – Greater Glasgow and Clyde – currently has 29, while the three island boards have 14 or 15 each.

Health and social care partnerships

The Scottish Government announced at the end of 2011 that health and social care partnerships would replace the 36 community health partnerships (CHPs) set up in 2005 to integrate primary and specialist services. CHPs were perceived to have suffered from division of accountability between the NHS and local authorities, insufficient and often unequal delegation of authority, budgets that were not integrated and poor clinical engagement.

Scottish Health Council

The Scottish Health Council exists to ensure the views of patients and the public are properly taken into account by NHS boards. It assesses how boards are involving patients in decisions about health services, develops examples of best practice in public involvement and helps patients give feedback to boards about their experiences of services. Although part of Healthcare Improvement Scotland, the council has its own identity and responsibilities, with a national office in Glasgow and local offices in each board area, where most of its staff are based. Members of the community are appointed to serve on a local advisory council for each NHS board area.
www.scottishhealthcouncil.org

Scottish Medicines Consortium (SMC)

The Scottish Medicines Consortium, an independent group within Healthcare Improvement Scotland, advises NHSScotland on the clinical and cost effectiveness of all newly licensed medicines, new formulations of existing medicines and all new conditions the medicines will treat. The SMC ensures that NHSScotland receives regular and standardised advice to enable it to introduce effective medicines as rapidly as possible. The SMC's decisions do not have statutory force, however, and it cannot insist that NHS boards prescribe a particular drug.
www.scottishmedicines.org

Healthcare Environment Inspectorate (HEI)

Set up in 2009, HEI is designed to maintain public confidence in all aspects of the care environment in Scottish hospitals. In particular, it has a mandate to ensure the correct procedures are followed to prevent the spread of healthcare-associated infections. Every acute hospital will receive at least one announced and one unannounced inspection within the three-year inspection cycle, with extra visits as required. HEI operates independently of the Scottish Government and NHS boards. It is based within Healthcare Improvement Scotland.

The new bodies will aim to integrate adult health and social care. They will be jointly accountable to the NHS and local authorities – as well as to the cabinet secretary for health – and work with the third and independent sectors. Each partnership will have a single jointly appointed senior accountable officer.

Health and social care partnerships will initially focus on improving older people's care by reducing delayed discharges and unplanned admissions to hospital, as well as enabling more older people to remain living in their own homes. NHS boards and local authorities will have to produce integrated budgets for older people's services and end 'cost-shunting'.

The creation of the new bodies will be subject to legislation in the Scottish Parliament.

Managed clinical networks

Managed clinical networks for a wide range of conditions became well established in Scotland before the rest of the UK. They are defined as:

> linked groups of health professionals and organisations from primary, secondary and tertiary care, working in a coordinated manner, unconstrained by existing professional and health board boundaries, to ensure equitable provision of high-quality clinically effective services throughout Scotland.

They are seen as an important way of integrating systems of care and developing clinical leadership. Managed care networks are a development of the concept, designed to cross boundaries between the NHS and social work departments.

www.mcns.nhsscotland.com

Strategy and policy

Bringing the NHS under the control of the Scottish Parliament has resulted in new directions for the Scottish health service distinct from policies pursued by the NHS in England. For example, NHSScotland has explicitly rejected market-based reforms introduced south of the border. This divergence has become more marked since opposing political parties have controlled the administrations in Holyrood and Westminster. With the Scottish National Party forming Scotland's first majority government in 2011, and with preparations to hold a referendum on independence, the NHS north and south of the border is likely to continue on different paths.

Since the SNP's first – minority – administration in 2007, population health improvement and the reversal of health inequalities have been strong policy themes across government. Its 2007 strategy, *Better health, better care*, continues to underlie the direction of policy. It lays great emphasis on seeing the public and staff as 'partners or co-owners' in 'a more mutual NHS', and promised not to change the funding model: 'In stressing public ownership through a more mutual approach, we distance NHSScotland still further from market orientated models'. Instead, 'cooperation and collaboration' are NHSScotland's guiding principles.

Notable policy differences between Scotland and England include:

Patient charter The Patient Rights (Scotland) Act 2011 places a duty on Scottish ministers to publish a charter of patient rights and responsibilities, which will be launched in October 2012. Other measures in the Act include:
- a 12-week treatment-time guarantee for planned and elective care on an inpatient or day case basis
- a patient advice and support service
- a legal right to complain.

Free personal care Uniquely in the UK, personal care services for people over 65 have been available free in Scotland since 2002; in the rest of the UK only nursing care is free. Personal care is defined as including help with personal hygiene, continence management, eating, simple treatments and personal assistance tasks. Local authorities' spending on providing personal care services to older people in their own homes has risen 139 per cent from £133 million in 2003/04 to £318 million in 2009/10. Spending on personal care and nursing care to self-funding residents in care homes has increased 25.6 per cent from £86 million to £108 million.

Minimum pricing of alcohol Scotland has already legislated to ban quantity discounts and restrict alcohol promotions; now the Scottish Parliament is considering a bill to set a minimum price for a unit of alcohol. It has strong support from public health directors in NHSScotland.

Other differences include:
- abolition of prescription charges in 2011, estimated to cost £57 million in 2011/12
- abolition of eye test charges in 2006, estimated to cost £91 million in 2010/11
- abolition of car-parking charges in 2009 at 14 hospitals, costing £1.4 million
- legislation for direct elections to NHS boards (see page 215)
- legislation to exclude 'commercial companies with shareholders' holding primary medical services contracts
- banning new private contracts for hospital cleaning and catering services.

Vital statistics: NHSScotland workforce September 2011

1 HCHS medical and dental: 13,336
2 Consultants: 4,719
3 Nursing and midwifery: 65,448
4 AHPs: 11,304
5 Admin staff: 28,859
6 Support staff: 18,767
7 Other: 12,108
   Total: 154,541

Source: ISD Scotland

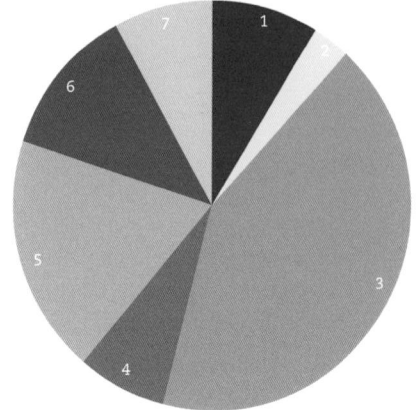

Spending (£ million)

	2011/12	2012/13
NHS and special health boards	8,645.1	8,862.3
Other health	2,723.6	2,720.7

Source: Scottish Government

Scotland's Health on the Web (SHOW)

This website is the official gateway to online information about NHSScotland.

www.show.scot.nhs.uk

12 The NHS in Wales

An awareness that Wales faces major health challenges has shaped its approach to providing care. It has high rates of cancer and heart disease and the highest proportion of elderly people of any of the four UK countries. Poverty levels are high in places, while services have to cater for a complex mix of rural, urban and valley areas.

The structure of NHS Wales

The Welsh Assembly Government took over ultimate responsibility for the NHS in Wales from Westminster in 1999. Two departments within the Welsh Government have strategic responsibility for health, one focusing on the NHS and social services, the other on public health matters. Significant structural change took place in the NHS in Wales in 2009. NHS Wales, like NHSScotland before it, has abolished the internal market and all but three specialist NHS trusts.

National Assembly for Wales

The National Assembly for Wales opened in 1999 and has 60 elected members (AMs). The UK Parliament devolved to it power to pass secondary legislation to develop and implement policies, make rules and regulations, set standards and issue guidance in areas including health and social services, housing, local government and education. Under the Government of Wales Act 2006, the Assembly's powers were strengthened to enable it to make laws, known as Measures, in devolved areas, with the agreement of the UK Parliament on a subject-by-subject basis. Following a referendum in March 2011, the people of Wales voted in favour of granting the Assembly further law-making powers. The Assembly is now able to pass laws on all subjects in the 20 devolved areas without first needing the agreement of the UK Parliament. Proposed laws are called Bills, and enacted laws will be called Acts.

The Welsh Government (known as the Welsh Assembly Government until May 2011) controls the management and performance of NHS Wales. It draws up strategic policies, sets priorities and allocates funds, but it is not currently able to raise extra taxes. The Assembly scrutinises and provides democratic control over the Welsh Government.

The Assembly's ten-member health and social care committee covers health, social care and NHS Wales. Membership reflects the balance of political groups within the Assembly.

Among other committees, the public accounts committee scrutinises the expenditure of NHS Wales by examining reports on its accounts prepared by the Auditor General for Wales, who heads the Wales Audit Office, created in 2005.

The Wales Office, led by the Secretary of State for Wales, represents Welsh interests in the UK Government and Parliament. There are 40 MPs at Westminster representing Welsh constituencies.

Further information
Welsh Government **www.wales.gov.uk**
National Assembly for Wales **www.assemblywales.org**
Wales Office **www.walesoffice.gov.uk**
Wales Audit Office **www.wao.gov.uk**

Welsh Government
The Welsh Government is the Assembly's executive body, led by the First Minister and a nine-strong cabinet that includes a minister for health and social services. The Government of Wales Act 2006 allows up to 12 ministers and deputy ministers, meaning the maximum size of the Welsh Government is 14, including the First Minister and Counsel General, who is the Government's chief legal adviser.

The First Minister is elected by AMs, and is therefore usually the leader of the largest party. Assembly elections are held every four years, the last being in May 2011 and resulting in a Welsh Labour-led Government. Of the Assembly's 60 members, 40 are elected in constituencies using the first-past-the-post system; the other 20 are elected to represent the five regions of Wales using the list system.

Further information
Welsh Government **http://new.wales.gov.uk**

Department for Health, Social Services and Children
The Department for Health, Social Services and Children is led by the minister for health and social services and is responsible for:
- advising the Welsh Government on health and social care policies and strategies
- contributing to health and social care legislation
- funding the NHS and other health and social care bodies
- managing and supporting the delivery of health and social care services
- monitoring and promoting improvements in service delivery.

Other responsibilities include research and development, finance, human resources, information management and technology, capital and estates. The department's director general of health and social services is also chief executive of NHS Wales and the accounting officer for the health service. The department's directorates and units are:
• community, primary care and health service policy directorate
• quality, standards and safety improvement directorate
• resources directorate
• children's health and social services directorate
• older people and long-term care policy directorate
• corporate management
• service delivery and performance
• strategy unit
• health and social services human resources
• Children and Family Court Advisory and Support Service in Wales.

The department's current priorities are:
• implementing local health, social care and wellbeing strategies to deliver integrated health and social care services
• improving health and quality of life
• reducing inequalities in personal health and access to services
• reducing waiting times
• implementing the quality plan for Wales to ensure safe, sustainable and accessible services
• implementing national standards of care for cancer, cardiac, children's, older people's, renal and diabetes services
• implementing policies which better reflect older people's needs
• implementing policies which safeguard children's needs.

Department for Public Health and Health Professions

The DPHHP is also led by the minister for health and social services, but its director is the chief medical officer for Wales. Formed in 2007 from the Office of the Chief Medical Officer and the Office of the Chief Nursing Officer, its objectives are:
• to protect the health of the people in Wales and prepare for health emergencies
• to improve health and reduce health inequalities
• to provide professional leadership for health and social care.

The existence of the DPHHP as a separate entity within the Welsh Government reflects the high priority attached to improving public health in Wales.

Wales: Local health boards

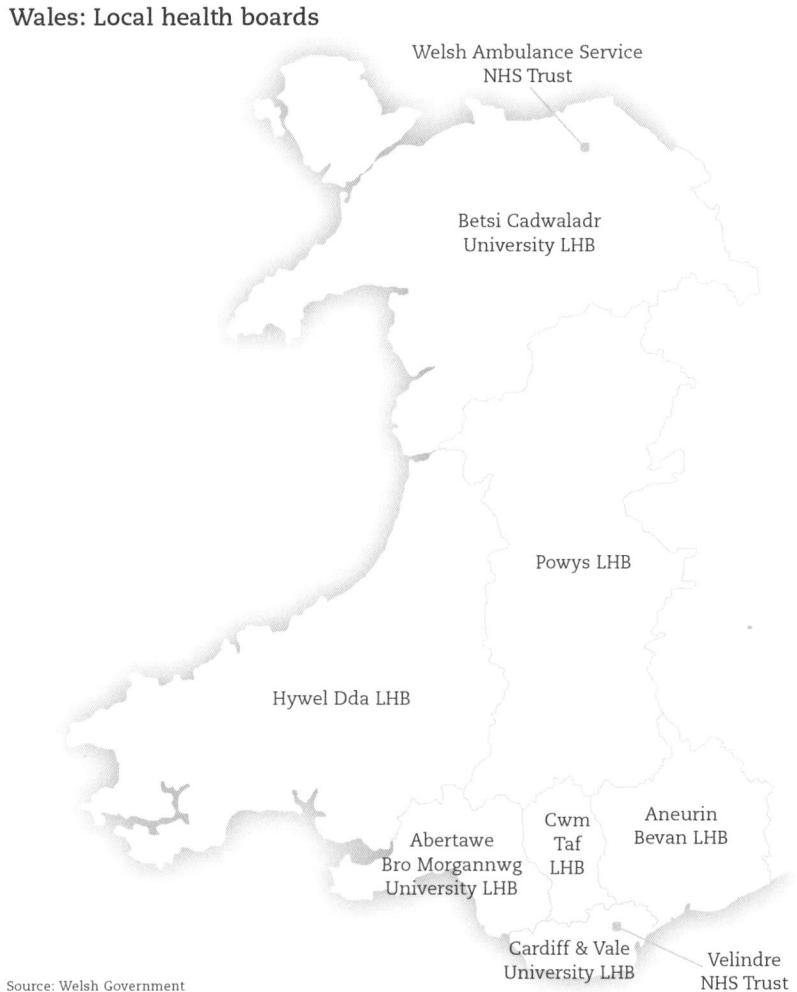

Welsh Ambulance Service NHS Trust

Betsi Cadwaladr University LHB

Powys LHB

Hywel Dda LHB

Cwm Taf LHB

Aneurin Bevan LHB

Abertawe Bro Morgannwg University LHB

Cardiff & Vale University LHB

Velindre NHS Trust

Source: Welsh Government

Restructuring NHS Wales

NHS Wales was reorganised in 2009, creating single local health organisations responsible for delivering all healthcare services within a geographical area, rather than the previous system of trusts and local health boards, which was dismissed as 'complex and over-bureaucratic'. Abolition of the internal market fulfilled a commitment made after the 2007 Assembly election. The Welsh Government hoped this would result in 'a more coordinated approach to healthcare delivery'. Commissioning has been replaced by a new planning system to 'integrate different elements of planning – service, workforce, estate and finance' – and benefit from 'strong clinical engagement throughout'.

Seven health boards replaced the 22 local health boards set up as commissioning bodies in 2004. The boards are responsible for:
• planning and designing
• developing and securing delivery of primary, community, secondary care, specialist and tertiary services
• identifying local needs within the national policy and standards framework set out by the minister.

Each has a decision-making corporate board, a stakeholder reference group and a professional forum; non-executives include representatives of universities, local government, third sector, trade unions and five independent members.

Seven trusts (already reduced from 14 to nine during 2008) were abolished and their staff, property and functions brought under health board control; NHS Wales has more than 130 hospitals and 15,000 beds. The Welsh Ambulance Services NHS Trust and Velindre NHS Trust, which manages specialist oncology services, remain. A third trust, the Public Health Wales NHS Trust (see below) was newly formed. Other features include:

National Advisory Board chaired by the minister and comprising the deputy minister, NHS chief executive, chief medical officer, director of social services, three representatives of local government, third sector and trade unions, and two independent members; responsible for offering the minister independent advice, it meets in public and publishes its papers

National Delivery Group chaired by NHS Wales' chief executive and comprising the DHSS senior directors and up to three independent members; it is responsible for boards' day-to-day operational performance

Public Health Wales NHS Trust bringing together in a single organisation a range of public health services and functions previously preformed by the National Public Health Service for Wales, Wales Centre for Health, Welsh Cancer Intelligence and Surveillance Unit and Screening Services Wales
www.publichealthwales.wales.nhs.uk

National Clinical Forum announced in 2011, this independent group of clinicians, chaired by NHS Wales' medical director, reviews health boards' plans for changing services to ensure they represent clinical best practice.

Healthcare Inspectorate Wales HIW was established in 2004 to ensure the safety and quality of health services by reviewing and inspecting standards in Welsh NHS bodies against a range of policies, guidance and regulations. Since 2006 it has also been the regulator for independent healthcare in Wales. It comprises a team of 50 based at Caerphilly and a pool of 200 external reviewers. HIW has rights to enter and inspect premises, as well as powers to require documents and information. www.hiw.org.uk

Eight community health councils – one for each health board area plus two for Powys – are statutory lay organisations with rights to information about, access to, and consultation with all NHS organisations on behalf of the public. The Welsh Government strengthened their powers in 2004. It is currently reviewing their governance and structure, and will consult on recommendations later in 2012.

Further information
NHS in Wales: why we are changing the structure, Welsh Government, October 2009.
Welsh NHS Confederation **www.welshconfed.org**

Strategy and policy
Although the NHS in Wales has had slightly different policy and structural arrangements from England for most of its existence, these have diverged more markedly since devolution in an attempt to find distinctively Welsh solutions for specifically Welsh problems. For example, it was the first in the UK to abolish all prescription charges, in 2007. Wales has some of the UK's highest rates of cancer, heart disease and deprivation, while part of its population suffers the worst health status in Europe.

After the 2007 Assembly election a policy document, *One Wales*, stated: 'We firmly reject the privatisation of NHS services or the organisation of such services on market models. We will guarantee public ownership, public funding and public control of this vital public service.'

The health minister set up the Bevan Commission in 2008 to act as a think tank and sounding board for three years, advising on emerging health issues. It aimed to ensure NHS Wales 'can draw on the best practice from across the world while remaining true to the principles of the NHS as established by Aneurin Bevan'. Its final report concluded that NHS Wales needed to involve the public in planning and prioritising services, drive out waste, ensure effective partnerships with local authorities and seek solutions to health problems across all policy agendas.

Further information
2008–2011 NHS Wales: forging a better future – a report by the Bevan Commission, Bevan Commission, May 2011.

Five-year vision
A five-year vision for NHS Wales, *Together for health*, contains measures that include:
- every health board setting targets for improving health
- the Welsh Government to publish delivery plans for major services such as cancer, cardiac care, stroke care and mental health, specifying the next steps in service improvement
- all district general hospitals retaining an essential role, although some of their services to change
- clinical networks of primary and community staff to support hospitals in providing care closer to home after patients' discharge from specialist centres, and make greater use of telemedicine to increase 24/7 access to services in rural areas
- annual reports on each major service area, including outcomes and patient satisfaction.

Further information
Together for health: a five-year vision for the NHS in Wales, Welsh Government, November 2011.

Rural health plan

Community hospitals form a centrepiece of the rural health plan for Wales. The plan seeks to 'add new purpose' to community hospitals and 'exploit their potential' to provide key services closer to rural communities. In addition, it proposes:

- a new 'rural practitioner' role – multi-skilled professionals who will cover services across NHS healthcare and social care
- a network of pharmacies in rural areas to improve access
- more use of telehealth and telecare so that patients do not have to travel long distances for routine treatment and checks
- a rural health innovation fund.

Further information

Rural health plan: improving integrated service delivery across Wales, Welsh Government, December 2009.

Strategic framework for public health

The Welsh Government published a strategic framework for public health. *Our healthy future* contains four aspirations for 2020:

- across society, people will take care and responsibility for their own and others' health and wellbeing
- organisations and individuals will work together to improve and protect health
- the gap between communities with poor and those with good health will be reduced
- healthy public policy will support and enable people to lead healthy lives.

Further information

Our healthy future, Welsh Government, May 2009.

Health in Wales

This website is the official gateway to online information about health and NHS services in Wales.

www.wales.nhs.uk

Vital statistics: NHS Wales workforce (WTE) September 2010

1 Medical and dental staff: 5,654
2 Nursing, midwifery and health visiting staff: 28,168
3 Administration and estates staff: 15,502
4 Scientific, therapeutic and technical staff: 11,483
5 Healthcare assistants and other support staff: 10,049
6 Ambulance staff: 1,429
7 Other: 159
   Total: 72,444

Source: Welsh Government

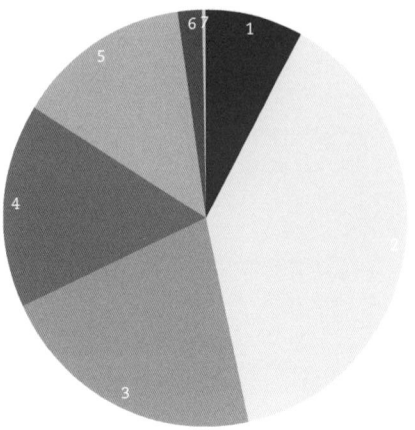

Spending (£ million) 2012/13

	REVENUE	CAPITAL	TOTAL
Total health, social services and children	6,046,623	240,603	**6,287,226**
Delivery of NHS services	5,491,962	230,279	**5,722,241**
Health central budgets	205,374	-	**-**
Public health and prevention	157,548	5,039	**162,587**
Social services	182,104	5,285	**187,389**
Cafcass Cymru	9,635	-	**-**

Source: Welsh Government

13 The NHS in Northern Ireland

Direct rule from Westminster between 2002 and 2007 restricted the healthcare reform process in Northern Ireland, but major restructuring took effect in 2007 and 2009. For almost 40 years, health and social services have been bound more closely together in Northern Ireland than in the rest of the UK, and under reforms announced at the end of 2011 look likely to be further integrated. Together they form the Province's largest employer. After more than three decades of the 'Troubles', Northern Ireland faces having to tackle in earnest its major health challenges. For example, it has some of the worst mental health problems in the UK and a particularly high suicide rate. It also faces a potentially major funding shortfall.

The structure of the NHS in Northern Ireland

Since October 1973, the NHS in Northern Ireland has been integrated with social services and is known as the Health and Social Care system (HSC). Accountability is to the Northern Ireland Assembly at Stormont via the minister who heads the Department of Health, Social Services and Public Safety. Five health and social care trusts and an ambulance trust provide services commissioned by a single regional health and social care board. www.hscni.net

Northern Ireland Assembly

The Northern Ireland Assembly was established as a result of the Belfast (or 'Good Friday') Agreement of 1998. It was elected later that year, operated in shadow form without government powers until full devolution in December 1999, but was then suspended in October 2002. Recalled in May 2006, under the St Andrews agreement it sat as a 'Transitional Assembly' to prepare for elections in March 2007 and restoration of full devolution in May 2007.

The Assembly has full legislative and executive authority for 'transferred matters', which include areas such as health, social care, education and agriculture. In addition, it may at a later date take responsibility for 'reserved matters'. 'Excepted matters' remain the UK Parliament's responsibility, and include defence, foreign policy and taxation.

The Assembly has 108 members (MLAs), six from each of Northern Ireland's 18 Westminster constituencies. Currently they represent eight political parties. A First Minister and a Deputy First Minister are elected to lead the ten-strong Executive Committee of Ministers. They have to stand for election jointly, and to be elected must have cross-community support. The parties elected to the Assembly choose ministerial portfolios and select ministers in proportion to their party strength. The Executive Committee brings forward proposals for new legislation in the form of Executive Bills for the Assembly to consider. It also sets out a programme for government each year, with an agreed budget for approval by the Assembly.

Twelve cross-party departmental committees have power to examine, debate and recommend changes to the Northern Ireland departments' policies and decisions. This includes, for example, how money is shared and spent. The health, social services and public safety committee advises and assists the minister of health, social services and public safety to formulate policy and undertakes scrutiny, policy development and consultation. It has 11 members.

Among the Assembly's six standing committees, the 11-strong public accounts committee's remit is to consider accounts covering the NHS in Northern Ireland. The committee has the power 'to send for persons, papers and records'.

The Northern Ireland Office, led by the Secretary of State for Northern Ireland, represents Northern Ireland's interests in the UK Government and Parliament. There are 18 MPs at Westminster representing Northern Ireland constituencies.
www.niassembly.gov.uk
www.nio.gov.uk

Northern Ireland Executive
The Executive forms the government of Northern Ireland and comprises 11 departments plus the Office of the First Minister and Deputy First Minister. Each department is headed by a minister who sits on the Assembly's Executive Committee. While devolution was suspended, the departments were run by the Northern Ireland Office.
www.northernireland.gov.uk

Department of Health, Social Services and Public Safety (DHSSPS)
The DHSSPS's mission is to improve the health and social wellbeing of people in Northern Ireland, by ensuring the provision of appropriate health and social care services in hospitals, GPs' surgeries and the community, through nursing, social work and other professional services. It also leads a major programme of cross-government action to improve health and wellbeing and reduce health inequalities.

The DHSSPS is responsible for:
- health and social care – including policy and legislation for hospitals, family practitioner services, community health and personal social services
- public health – policy and legislation to promote and protect the health and wellbeing of Northern Ireland's population
- public safety – policy and legislation for food safety, emergency planning, fire and rescue services.

Its main functions are:
- determining and reviewing policy
- setting standards, priorities and targets
- overseeing the safety and quality of services
- HSC workforce planning, education and training
- HSC capital investment
- financial planning and control
- regional performance management
- overseeing the governance of Northern Ireland's 17 HSC organisations.

The permanent secretary is also chief executive of the HSC system, as well as principal accounting officer for all the DHSSPS's responsibilities. In addition, five professional groups are each led by a chief professional officer:
- medical and allied services
- social services inspectorate
- nursing and midwifery advisory group
- dental services
- pharmaceutical advice and services.

The DHSSPS is the largest of Northern Ireland's 12 departments, accounting for two-fifths of the Northern Ireland budget.
www.dhsspsni.gov.uk

Health and social care system
Health and social care in Northern Ireland were reorganised in 2009. The main components of the system include:

Health and Social Care Board (HSCB) which is responsible for commissioning services, resource management, performance management and service improvement.
www.hscboard.hscni.net

Five local commissioning groups which, as statutory committees of the HSCB, involve primary care professionals in planning and resourcing services, covering the same geographical area as the five trusts, with membership including four GPs, a pharmacist, dentist, four elected representatives, two social care professionals, a nurse, a public health professional, an allied health professional and two voluntary sector representatives.

Six health and social care trusts one of which is the ambulance service, manage and administer hospitals, health centres, residential homes, day centres and other health and social care facilities.

Public Health Agency whose key functions are improving health and wellbeing and health protection, as well as providing professional input to the commissioning process; it is jointly responsible with the HSCB for developing a commissioning plan, and works with local government and others to improve health and wellbeing and reduce health inequalities. www.publichealth.hscni.net

Regulation and Quality Improvement Authority (RQIA) an independent body responsible for monitoring and inspecting the availability and quality of health and social care services through registration and inspection. www.rqia.org.uk

Patient and Client Council a regional body with local offices covering the geographical areas of the five health and social care trusts, its objective is to provide a powerful, independent voice for patients, clients, carers and communities on health and social care issues. www.patientclientcouncil.hscni.net

Business Services Organisation provides support functions for the entire system, including administrative support, financial services, human resources, personnel and corporate services, training, estates, information technology and information management, procurement of goods and services, legal services, internal audit and fraud prevention. www.hscbusiness.hscni.net

The system also includes the Northern Ireland Practice and Education Council (NIPEC), Northern Ireland Social Care Council (NISCC) and Northern Ireland Medical and Dental Training Agency (NIMDTA).

Strategy and policy

Given Northern Ireland's unique geographical and political circumstances within the UK, it is to be expected that the NHS there has distinct characteristics – most notably that integration of health and social care has been a longstanding feature. While spending per head on health and social care is higher in Northern Ireland than in England, outputs and outcomes have lagged behind. Although this may be partly due to inefficiency, and therefore perhaps susceptible to reform, other reasons may include acknowledged greater needs, better quality of provision, the need to maintain hospitals in rural locations and the higher costs of delivering services in deprived areas.

Like Scotland and Wales, Northern Ireland has abolished prescription charges – since 2010 in its case, costing about £13 million a year. However, given current financial constraints, it is now contemplating reintroducing them after research by the Patient and Client Council in 2011 found that a minimum prescription charge would be acceptable with exemptions for people with long-term conditions and with patients' economic and social situation taken into account.

The independent review of health and social care in Northern Ireland, carried out in 2005 by Professor John Appleby in the manner of the Wanless reports in England and Wales (see page 167), concluded that 'a significant increase in resources' would be needed as well as major productivity improvements. A follow-up report in 2011 found a looming funding gap of £1 billion after the 2010 spending review (see page 168) and a productivity shortfall worth another £1 billion. It also noted that Northern Ireland had over 20 per cent more acute beds than England, but throughput was 25 per cent lower. Waiting lists for inpatients and outpatients were rising rapidly since significant falls from 2006 to 2009.

After the Assembly elections in 2011, the new health and social services minister set up a review of HSC services led by the HSCB chief executive. Among the 99 recommendations in its report, *Transforming your care*, are:
- creation of 17 integrated care partnerships to.enable closer working within and between hospital and community services
- shifting 4 per cent (£83 million) of funding from hospitals to primary, community and social care services
- reducing Northern Ireland's ten acute hospitals to between five and seven.

The minister intends to set up a strategic programme board to oversee the changes, which will be implemented over five years.

Further information

Rapid review of Northern Ireland Health and Social Care funding needs and the productivity challenge 2011/12–2014/15, Professor John Appleby/DHSSPS, March 2011.

People's views about prescription charging and products available on prescription, Patient and Client Council, June 2011.

Transforming your care: a review of health and social care in Northern Ireland, HSC, December 2011.

HSC in Northern Ireland

This website is the official gateway to health and social care services in Northern Ireland.

www.hscni.net

Vital statistics: HSC in Northern Ireland workforce March 2011

1 Medical and dental: 3,916
2 Nursing and midwifery: 16,012
3 Professional and technical: 7,316
4 Ambulance: 1,047
5 Admin and clerical: 12,067
6 Estates services: 661
7 Support services: 6,693
8 Nurse support staff: 4,528
9 Social services: 7,480
10 Home helps: 5,221
11 Other: 80
   Total: 65,021

Source: DHSSPS

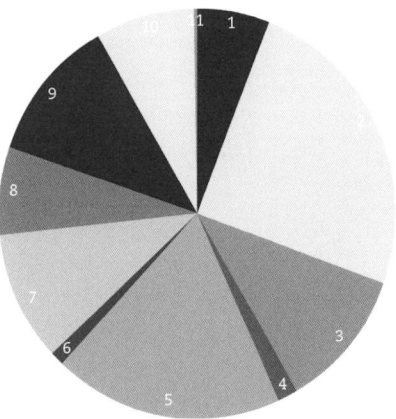

Spending (£ million)

	2011/12	2012/13	% CHANGE
Revenue	4,308.6	4,371.5	1.5
Capital	197.5	273.3	38.4

Source: Northern Ireland Executive

14 The NHS in Europe

The European Union now represents 27 countries and almost 500 million people. It is governed by a series of treaties negotiated at intergovernmental conferences and ratified by each member state. Its work is carried out by different institutions – from the Council of Ministers to the European Commission, European Parliament and European Court of Justice.

It is estimated that at least half the laws enacted in the UK stem from EU legislation. The EU's work on health has developed substantially over the last 15 years. In the past, health policy was seen as very much the responsibility of member states, and little work took place at EU level, but especially since 2000 the EU has aimed for a more coordinated approach. Developments in the single European market and rulings in the European Court have also had an important impact on healthcare systems. The NHS needs to keep abreast of developments in Europe and seek to influence them when appropriate.

Key organisation: **NHS European Office**
The NHS European Office was established in 2007 because of the increasing impact of EU policy and legislation on the NHS. Based in Brussels and London, it is part of the NHS Confederation. Its main activities are:
• monitoring EU policy and legislative developments important to the NHS
• informing NHS organisations of EU developments, including funding opportunities
• influencing EU proposals in the NHS's interest
• organising study visits to learn about good practice in other European countries
• facilitating European peer links between groups of healthcare professionals
• raising the NHS's profile and promoting its expertise and good practice in Europe.

Further information
Representing the NHS in Europe: three years of achievement, NHS European Office, November 2010.
www.nhsconfed.org/europe

The European Union

Member states

1 Austria
2 Belgium
3 Bulgaria
4 Cyprus
5 Czech Republic
6 Denmark
7 Estonia
8 Finland
9 France
10 Germany
11 Greece
12 Hungary

13 Ireland
14 Italy
15 Latvia
16 Lithuania
17 Luxembourg
18 Malta
19 Netherlands
20 Poland
21 Portugal
22 Romania
23 Slovakia
24 Slovenia

25 Spain
26 Sweden
27 United Kingdom

Candidate countries

28 Croatia
29 Macedonia
30 Turkey

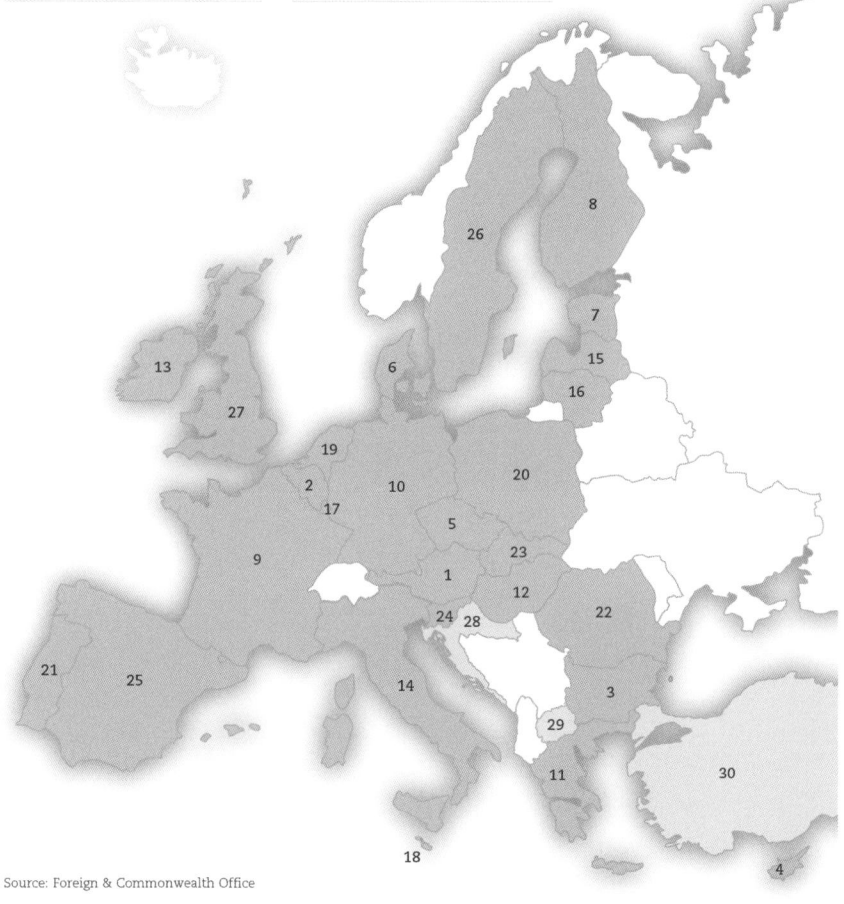

Source: Foreign & Commonwealth Office

European Commission

The Commission is the EU's executive arm, responsible for formulating policies, initiating legislation and the day-to-day running of the EU. It comprises a president and 27 commissioners, each leading a directorate and supported by 38,000 civil servants – administrative officials, policy experts, translators, interpreters and secretarial staff. Since 2000 it has had a directorate for health and consumers.
http://ec.europa.eu

Council of the European Union

Sometimes called the Council of Ministers, this defines the EU's overall political direction and priorities. It has a president elected by Council members – EU member countries – who serves for two and a half years. The Council meets in various formations to discuss different policy areas. Meetings are attended by the relevant minister from each country's national government, and decisions are usually taken by either qualified majority – voting weighted to take account of population size – or unanimity. Health ministers usually meet once every six months as part of the Employment, Social Policy, Health and Consumer Affairs Council.
www.consilium.europa.eu

European Parliament

This is the directly elected parliamentary body of the EU. With the Council of Ministers, it forms the legislative branch of the EU institutions. It has over 700 members, who are elected proportionally from the member states every five years. MEPs sit in political groups, and not as national delegations. Elections last took place in 2009, when the UK chose 72 MEPs. Most EU legislation is passed according to 'co-decision', under which the Parliament and Council amend and approve it jointly. Where co-decision does not apply, the Parliament has the right to be consulted on legislation. It also holds other EU institutions to account – for example, by asking parliamentary questions – and can reject or censure the Commission and the EU budget.
www.europarl.europa.eu

European Courts

The EU's judicial branch comprises the European Court of Justice (ECJ) and the Court of First Instance. Together they interpret and apply EU law and treaties, ensuring consistency throughout Europe. The Court of First Instance mainly deals with cases taken by individuals and companies, and the ECJ deals with cases taken by member states, other EU institutions and those referred to it by the courts of member states. Judgements from the European Courts are legally binding and must be implemented throughout the EU, even if they establish rights in areas previously without EU legislation.
http://curia.europa.eu

EU health policy

While the organisation, financing and management of healthcare remain the national responsibility of member countries, the EU undertakes health-related activities – in particular, fostering cooperation on protecting and promoting public health and enabling the free movement of people.

EU policy and legislation have a substantial impact on the NHS as a provider and commissioner of healthcare, as a major employer and as a business. Developments in internal market rules, employment law, competition legislation and environment and energy policy and legislation must all be considered in parallel with EU health policy to determine potential implications for the NHS.

For example, European Court rulings clarifying how EU internal market rules apply to health services have a wide-reaching impact on the NHS. The European Health Insurance Card (EHIC), created under EU arrangements for cooperation on social security, allows citizens access to urgent healthcare when travelling in the EU. And the Working Time Directive, designed to protect workers' health and safety, has had a significant impact on healthcare organisations throughout the EU.

EU health strategy

Although the scope for legislation in health policy is limited, the EU can adopt initiatives to promote and improve health, and this provides the basis for its official health strategy launched in 2000, revised in 2007 and intended to last until 2013. The strategy sets the direction of EU activities in health by establishing some core principles: taking a value-driven approach, recognising the links between health and economic prosperity, integrating health in all policies and strengthening the EU's voice in global health. It also sets the main strategic objectives for action: fostering good health in an ageing Europe, protecting citizens from health threats and creating dynamic health systems and new technologies.

The EU approach emphasises coordination and cooperation, especially on disease prevention. Examples of traditional EU-wide public health work include joint action to address major diseases such as cancer and HIV/AIDS, coordinating efforts to combat communicable diseases, and major campaigns against drug abuse.

The strategy recognises that huge differences in health exist between and within member states. It affirms the importance of tackling health inequalities and working across different sectors. It also recognises the importance of patient empowerment and of focusing on health determinants.

A mid-term evaluation of the strategy found that it had had only limited influence on member states' health policies.

The European Commission has proposed that the next strategy lays greater emphasis on the links between economic growth and a healthy population.

Further information
Together for health: a strategic approach for the EU 2008–2013, European Commission, October 2007.
Report on the mid-term evaluation of the EU health strategy, Public Health Evaluation and Impact Assessment Consortium, October 2011.
Proposal for a regulation of the European Parliament and of the Council on establishing a Health for Growth Programme, the third multi-annual programme of EU action in the field of health for the period 2014–2020, European Commission, November 2011.

Cross-border healthcare
Cross-border care is a growing trend, particularly for countries in mainland Europe. Test cases in the European Court of Justice concerning patients seeking reimbursement for cross-border care drove developments for ten years. One case in 2003 concerned a UK patient who sought reimbursement from the NHS for £3,900 for a hip replacement carried out in France after being told she would have to wait a year for the operation in Britain.

Rulings created an ambiguous situation, defending both citizens' right to seek healthcare abroad and the health systems' ability to defend financial stability. The court stipulated that provisions in the EU's treaties on free movement of services applied to healthcare regardless of how it was organised or financed – and confirmed this was so even for a tax-funded system like the NHS. It had therefore established patients' right to receive healthcare in another EU member state and to be reimbursed by their own healthcare system, but it remained unclear how this right was to be implemented in practice.

As a result, citizens remained unclear about their entitlement to healthcare abroad or how they might go about identifying, comparing and choosing providers. Member states were unclear about how to regulate and plan their systems without creating unjustified obstacles to free movement. Now a new EU law has clarified the situation, with significant implications for NHS commissioners and providers.

European directive on cross-border healthcare
The EU directive on cross-border healthcare was adopted in March 2011 and will have to be implemented in the UK by October 2013. Its rationale is that it should be as easy as possible for patients who want access to healthcare abroad to have it, subject to the same conditions that apply to treatment at home.

Key points for commissioners include:
- NHS patients have the right to seek in another European country any healthcare they would have received under the NHS and to be reimbursed up to the amount their treatment would have cost the NHS
- patients pay the difference if care abroad is more expensive, plus their travel and other costs
- patients do not have rights to reimbursement for treatment they would not have received under the NHS
- patients are subject to the same conditions that apply when accessing NHS treatment: for example, a patient wanting to see a specialist abroad would still need a GP referral
- prior authorisation may only be introduced for healthcare subject to planning requirements and involving a hospital stay or use of highly specialised, cost-intensive medical equipment
- prior authorisation cannot be refused if a patient is experiencing 'undue delay' in receiving NHS care
- commissioners must ensure cross-border patients can access follow-up healthcare on returning to the UK
- commissioners may pay directly for healthcare in another European country if this would benefit the patient.

Key points for providers include:
- NHS, independent and third sector providers treating European patients can be paid directly by the patient or through the patient's home system
- providers cannot discriminate against European patients by applying different quality and safety standards or higher charges
- it is not yet clear how costs will be calculated and whether NHS tariffs could be topped up to account for additional costs only applying to European patients
- providers are liable for the healthcare they provide: European patients unhappy with their care or who have suffered harm may complain and seek compensation according to UK rules and procedures
- no provider is required to accept EU patients to the detriment of home patients – particularly relevant for NHS organisations offering highly specialised services for which a surge of demand could increase waiting times for NHS patients.

The directive is the first genuine example of EU legislation specifically in the area of healthcare services, traditionally the sole preserve of national governments. Its implementation in the UK will take place in parallel with the reorganisation of the NHS in England, raising questions about how the rules will be interpreted and which organisations will be responsible for which provisions.

Further information
Briefing 7: Patient choice beyond borders – implications of the EU directive on cross-border healthcare for NHS commissioners and providers, NHS European Office, May 2011.

Current EU policy initiatives
Issues currently under consideration include:

Working Time Directive
Negotiations have begun to revise the European Working Time Directive. Employers and trade unions met formally at EU level for the first time in December 2011. Talks are expected to cover key issues for the NHS, such as the way on-call time is counted and rest periods are enforced. The NHS European Office says healthcare staff should maintain the right to opt out of the 48-hour ceiling on working hours so that the NHS can provide a properly staffed service and safe continuity of care.

Procurement rules
The European Commission has proposed new rules for public procurement in the EU, designed to streamline public purchasing and create a special regime for health service contracts over 500,000 euros.

Mobility of health professionals
The European Commission has published proposals intending to make it easier for people to practise in other European countries, but recognising that more stringent measures need to apply to health professionals to protect patients.

Clinical trials
A revised EU Clinical Trials Directive is expected in mid-2012, regulating the administrative requirements and ethical soundness of trials, as well as the safety of participants. It is hoped that the new proposals will go further in encouraging clinical research through a streamlined and risk-proportionate approach to clinical trials.

Medical devices
The recent breast implant scandal has raised questions over how the EU regulatory framework governing the marketing and surveillance of medical devices could be strengthened to ensure greater protection for patients. New EU proposals are expected in 2012.

Further information
www.nhsconfed.org/europe – for information on each of the above and other EU policy developments and their potential implications for the NHS.
Reforming public procurement: EU proposals for a new public procurement Directive, NHS European Office, February 2012.
Mobility of health professionals across Europe – 2012: crunch time for recognition of professional qualifications, NHS European Office, February 2012.

Acronym buster

ABHI	Association of British Healthcare Industries
ABPI	Association of the British Pharmaceutical Industry
AC	Audit Commission
ACCEA	Advisory Committee on Clinical Excellence Awards
ACDP	Advisory Committee on Dangerous Pathogens
ACEVO	Association of Chief Executives of Voluntary Organisations
ACRA	Advisory Committee on Resource Allocation
ADASS	Association of Directors of Adult Social Services
A&E	accident and emergency
AfC	Agenda for Change
AHP	allied health profession
AHSC	academic health science centre
AHSN	academic health science network
ALB	arm's-length body
ALE	auditors' local evaluation
ALTO	arm's-length trading organisation
AM	Assembly Member (Wales)
AME	annually managed expenditure
AMRC	Academy of Medical Royal Colleges
APMS	alternative provider medical services
AQP	any qualified provider
AWP	any willing provider
BDA	British Dental Association
BIS	(Department for) Business, Innovation and Skills
BMA	British Medical Association
BME	black and minority ethnic
BNF	British National Formulary
BRC	biomedical research centre
BROMI	Better Regulation of Medicines Initiative
BRU	biomedical research unit
CAMHS	child and adolescent mental health services
CAS	Central Alerting System
CAT	computerised axial tomography (scan)
CBT	cognitive behavioural therapy
CCG	clinical commissioning group
CCP	Co-operation and Competition Panel
CCP	critical care paramedic
CDO	chief dental officer
CDU	clinical decision unit
CEAC	Clinical and Excellence Awards Committee (Northern Ireland)

CEMACH	Confidential Enquiry into Maternal and Child Health
CFH	(NHS) Connecting for Health
CfPS	Centre for Public Scrutiny
CfWI	Centre for Workforce Intelligence
CHCP	community health and care partnership (Scotland)
CHD	coronary heart disease
CHI	community health index (Scotland)
CHMS	community health and miscellaneous services
CHP	community health partnership (Scotland)
CIC	community interest company
CIMP	clinical information management programme
CIO	chief information officer
CIP	cost improvement programme
CLAHRC	collaboration for leadership in applied health research and care
CLG	(Department of) Communities and Local Government
CME	continuing medical education
CMHT	community mental health team
CMO	chief medical officer
CNO	chief nursing officer
CNST	Clinical Negligence Scheme for Trusts
CO	Cabinet Office
COMARE	Committee on Medical Aspects of Radiation in the Environment
COMEAP	Committee on the Medical Effects of Air Pollutants
COSLA	Convention of Scottish Local Authorities
CPA	care programme approach
CPD	continuing professional development
CPN	community psychiatric nurse
CPR	Child Protection Register
CQC	Care Quality Commission
CQUIN	Commissioning for Quality and Innovation
CRD	Centre for Research and Dissemination
CRS	(NHS) Care Records Service
CSA	Common Services Agency (Scotland)
CSO	chief scientific officer
CSO	civil society organisation
CSP	Chartered Society of Physiotherapy
CSR	comprehensive spending review
CTO	compulsory treatment order
DAT	drug action team
DCMS	Department for Culture, Media and Sport
DDRB	doctors and dentists (pay) review body
DECC	Department of Energy and Climate Change

DEFRA	Department for Environment, Food and Rural Affairs
DEL	departmental expenditure limit
DES	directed enhanced services
DfE	Department for Education
DFP	Department of Finance and Personnel (Northern Ireland)
DfT	Department for Transport
DFT	distance from target
DGH	district general hospital
DH or DoH	Department of Health
DHSSPS	Department of Health, Social Services and Public Safety (Northern Ireland)
DMB	departmental management board (Department of Health)
DMS	Defence Medical Services
DNR	do not resuscitate
DPH	director of public health
DPHHP	Department for Public Health and Health Professions (Wales)
DPR	Data Protection Registrar
DRE	delivering race equality
DSO	departmental strategic objective
DSSA	delivering same-sex accommodation
DSU	day surgery unit
DTC	diagnosis and treatment centre
DTOC	delayed transfer of care
DWP	Department for Work and Pensions
EAU	emergency assessment unit
EBH	evidence-based healthcare
EBM	evidence-based medicine
ECCT	extended community care team (NHSScotland)
ECHR	European Convention on Human Rights
ECJ	European Court of Justice
E&D	equality and diversity
EDC	(NHS) Equality and Diversity Council
EDS	(NHS) Equality Delivery System
EFL	external financing limit
e-GIF	(electronic) government interoperability framework
EHIC	European Health Insurance Card
EHPF	European Health Policy Forum
EHR	electronic health record
EI	early intervention
EIP	early intervention in psychosis
EME	efficacy and mechanism evaluation
ENT	ear, nose and throat

EO	employers' organisation
EPP	Expert Patient Programme
EPR	electronic patient record
EPS	Electronic Prescription Service
ERDB	England Revalidation Delivery Board
ERDIP	Electronic Record Development and Implementation Programme
ERIC	Estates Return Information Collection
ESR	electronic staff record
ETP	electronic transmission of prescriptions
ETS	emissions trading scheme (EU)
EWTD	European Working Time Directive
FCE	finished consultant episode
FHS	family health services
FMP	financial management programme
FNP	family nurse partnership
FOI	freedom of information
FPNC	free personal and nursing care (NHSScotland)
FSA	Food Standards Agency
FT	foundation trust
FTN	Foundation Trust Network
GDC	General Dental Council
GDS	general dental services
GMC	General Medical Council
GMS	general medical services
GOS	general ophthalmic services
GPC	(BMA) General Practitioners Committee
GPhC	General Pharmaceutical Council
GPSI or **GPwSI**	general practitioner with a special interest
GSCC	General Social Care Council
GTAC	Gene Therapy Advisory Committee
GTN	(UK) Genetic Testing Network
GWC	General Whitley Council
HA	health authority
HB	health board
HCA	healthcare assistant
HCAI	healthcare-associated infection
HCHS	hospital and community health services
HCW	Health Commission Wales
HDL	Health Department letter
HEAT	health efficiency access treatment (targets – Scotland)

HEE	Health Education England
HEFCE	Higher Education Funding Council for England
HEI	higher education institution
HEI	Healthcare Environment Inspectorate (Scotland)
HENSE	Health and Education National Strategic Exchange
HES	hospital episode statistics
HFEA	Human Fertilisation and Embryology Authority
HGC	Human Genetics Commission
HIA	health impact assessment
HIEC	health innovation and education cluster
HIS	Health Improvement Scotland
HIW	Healthcare Inspectorate Wales
HLE	healthy life expectancy
HMO	health maintenance organization (US)
HoNOS	Health of the Nation Outcome Scales
HOSC	health overview and scrutiny committee
HPA	Health Protection Agency
HPC	Health Professions Council
HPMA	Healthcare People Management Association
HPU	health protection unit
HQIP	Healthcare Quality Improvement Partnership
HRG	healthcare resource group
HSC	(House of Commons) health select committee
HSC	health and social care (Northern Ireland)
HSCI	health service cost index
HS&DR	health services and delivery research
HSE	Health and Safety Executive
HSE	Health Survey for England
HSJ	Health Service Journal
HSR	health service research
HTA	health technology assessment
HTC	healthcare technology cooperative
HWB	health and wellbeing board
i4i	invention for innovation research
IAPT	improving access to psychological therapies
IC	information commissioner
ICAS	independent complaints advocacy service
ICD	international classification of diseases
ICO	integrated care organisation
ICP	integrated care pathway
ICR	(NHS) injury costs recovery (scheme)
ICT	information and communication technology

ICU	intensive care unit
IMAS	Interim Management and Support
IMCA	independent mental capacity advocate
IM&T	information management and technology
IP	inpatient
IPR	individual performance review
IQI	indicators for quality improvement
IRP	Independent Reconfiguration Panel
ISB	(NHS) Information Standards Board
ISD	Information and Statistics Division (Scotland)
ISTC	independent sector treatment centre
JHWS	joint health and wellbeing strategy
JIP	joint investment plan
JSNA	joint strategic needs assessment
KSF	(NHS) knowledge and skills framework
LAL	local authority letter
LES	local enhanced services
LETB	local education and training board
LGA	Local Government Association
LHB	local health board (Wales)
LINks	local involvement networks
LIS	local implementation strategy
LIT	local implementation team
LTA	long-term agreement
LTC	long-term condition
MAU	medical assessment unit
MCN	managed clinical network
MCO	managed care organisation
MDHU	Ministry of Defence hospital unit
MEE	Medical Education England
MERIT	medical emergency response incident teams
MFF	market forces factor
MHMDS	mental health minimum dataset
MHRA	Medicines and Healthcare Products Regulatory Agency
MHRT	mental health review tribunal
MiP	Managers in Partnership
MLA	Member of the Legislative Assembly (Northern Ireland)
MMC	Modernising Medical Careers
MMR	measles, mumps, rubella
MoJ	Ministry of Justice
MPET	multi-professional education and training
MPIG	minimum practice income guarantee

MQI	Measuring for Quality Improvement
MRC	Medical Research Council
MRI	magnetic resonance imaging
MRSA	methicillin-resistant *Staphylococcus aureus*
MSC	modernising scientific careers
MSP	Member of the Scottish Parliament
MST	multi-systemic therapy
MTS	(NHS) management training scheme
N3	new national network
NAGCAE	National Advisory Group on Clinical Audit and Enquiries
NAO	National Audit Office
NAW	National Assembly for Wales
NBAP	national booked admissions programme
NCAF	National Clinical Audit Forum
NCAPOP	National Clinical Audit and Patients' Outcomes Programme
NCAS	National Clinical Assessment Service
NCASP	National Clinical Audit Support Programme
NCE	national confidential enquiry
NCEPOD	National Confidential Enquiry into Perioperative Deaths
NCVO	National Council for Voluntary Organisations
NDPB	non-departmental public body
NED	non-executive director
NES	national enhanced services
NES	NHS Education for Scotland
NHSBSA	NHS Business Services Authority
NHSBT	NHS Blood and Transplant
NHSCB	NHS Commissioning Board
NHSI	NHS Institute for Innovation and Improvement
NHSLA	NHS Litigation Authority
NHS LIFT	NHS Local Improvement Finance Trust
NHST	NHS trust
NHS TEF	NHS Transitional Executive Forum
NIA	Northern Ireland Assembly
NIAO	Northern Ireland Audit Office
NIC	national insurance contribution
NIC	(NHS) National Innovation Centre
NICE	National Institute for Health and Clinical Excellence
NIGB	National Information Governance Board
NIHR	National Institute for Health Research
NIO	Northern Ireland Office
NLIAH	National Leadership and Innovation Agency for Healthcare (Wales)

NLOP	National Programme for IT local ownership programme
NLPH	National Library for Public Health
NMC	Nursing and Midwifery Council
NOF	New Opportunities Fund
NOG	National Oversight Group (for high-security hospitals)
NPDG	National PALS Development Group
NPfIT	National Programme for IT (in the NHS)
NPG	national priorities guidance
NPSA	National Patient Safety Agency
NQB	National Quality Board
NRAC	NHSScotland Resource Allocation Committee
NRCI	national reference cost index
NRES	National Research Ethics Service
NRLS	National Reporting and Learning Service
NRT	nicotine replacement therapy
NSF	national service framework
NSRC	national schedule of reference costs
NSS	National Services Scotland
NTA	National Treatment Agency (for Substance Misuse)
NTAC	NHS Technology Adoption Centre
NTDA	NHS Trust Development Authority
NTO	national training organisation
NWP	(NHS) National Workforce Projects
OCPA	Office of the Commissioner for Public Appointments
ODP	operating department practitioner
OFMDFM	Office of the First Minister & Deputy First Minister (Northern Ireland)
OGC	Office of Government Commerce
OHE	Office of Health Economics
OLS	Office for Life Sciences
ONS	Office for National Statistics
OP	outpatient
OSC	(local authority) overview and scrutiny committee
OSCHR	Office for Strategic Co-ordination of Health Research
OT	occupational therapist/therapy
OTC	over-the-counter
PAB	professional advisory board
PAC	(House of Commons) public accounts committee
PACS	picture archiving and communications systems
PAF	performance assessment framework
PALS	patient advice and liaison service
PASS	Patient Advice and Support Service (Scotland)

PBC	practice-based commissioning
PbR	payment by results
PCIP	primary care investment plan
PCO	primary care organisation
PCT	primary care trust
PDP	personal development plan
PEC	professional executive committee (of PCT)
PFD	personal, fair and diverse
PFI	private finance initiative
PHE	Public Health England
PHO	public health observatory
PHR	public health research
PIG	policy implementation guide
PLICS	patient level information and costing
P-MERIT	paramedic medical emergency response incident teams
PMS	personal medical services
PPC	(prescription) pre-payment certificate
PPE	patient and public engagement
PPF	priorities and planning framework
PPI	patient and public involvement
PPO	preferred provider organisation
PPP	public–private partnership
PPRS	Pharmaceutical Price Regulation Scheme
PRB	pay review body
PROM	patient-reported outcome measure
PRP	policy research programme
PSS	personal social services
QA	quality assurance
QALY	quality-adjusted life year
QIPP	quality innovation productivity and prevention
QMAS	quality management and analysis system
QOF	quality and outcomes framework
RAB	resource accounting and budgeting
RCD	research capacity development
RCGP	Royal College of General Practitioners
RCM	Royal College of Midwives
RCN	Royal College of Nursing
RCP	Royal College of Physicians
RCPE	Royal College of Physicians of Edinburgh
RCPSG	Royal College of Physicians and Surgeons of Glasgow
RCS	Royal College of Surgeons
RCSE	Royal College of Surgeons of Edinburgh

RCT	randomised controlled trial
RfPB	research for patient benefit
RGH	rural general hospital (NHSScotland)
RN	registered nurse
ROCR	Review of Central Returns
RST	(NHS) Revalidation Support Team
RTA	road traffic accident
RTT	referral to treatment
SACDA	Scottish Advisory Committee on Distinction Awards
SARS	severe acute respiratory syndrome
SAS	Scottish Ambulance Service
SAS	staff and associated specialist (doctors)
SASM	Scottish Audit of Surgical Mortality
SBS	(NHS) Shared Business Services
SCG	specialised commissioning group
SCI	Scottish care information
SCIE	Social Care Institute for Excellence
SCR	summary care record
SCVO	Scottish Council for Voluntary Organisations
SDO	service delivery and organisation
SDU	(NHS) Sustainable Development Unit
SEIF	Social Enterprise Investment Fund
SFA	statement of fees and allowances
SGHD	Scottish Government health directorates
SHA	strategic health authority (and special health authority)
SHMI	summary hospital-level mortality indicator
SHO	senior house officer
SHOW	Scottish Health on the Web
SHRINE	Strategic Human Resources Information Network
SHTG	Scottish Health Technologies Group
SIGN	Scottish Intercollegiate Guidelines Network
SLA	service level agreement
SMC	Scottish Medicines Consortium
SMR	standardised mortality ratio
SNOMED	systematised nomenclature of medicine
SPF	Social Partnership Forum
SPI	Scientific Pandemic Influenza Advisory Committee
SPMS	specialist provider medical services
SRP	structural reform plan
SSA	standard spending assessment
SSC	shared service centre
ST&T	scientific, therapeutic and technical (staff)

TaMHS	targeted mental health in schools
TFA	tripartite formal agreement
TUPE	Transfer of Undertakings (Protection of Employment) Regulations 1981
UKCC	UK Cochrane Centre
UKCRC	UK Clinical Research Collaboration
UKCRN	UK Clinical Research Network
VCS	voluntary and community sector
VFM	value for money
VTE	venous thrombo-embolism
WAG	Welsh Assembly Government
WAO	Wales Audit Office
WHO	World Health Organization
WORD	Wales Office of Research and Development for Health and Social Care
WPF	Welsh Partnership Forum
WRT	workforce review team
WTD	Working Time Directive
WTR	working time regulations

Index

Acknowledgements

The NHS Confederation is grateful to all those involved in the production of this edition of *The NHS handbook* (formerly known before 2008 as the pocket guide). Particular thanks are due to:

- our sponsor, NHS Professionals
- those who have supported the guide through advertising (listed below)
- those organisations that have kindly allowed us to reproduce diagrams and other materials
- Grade Design, for designing and typesetting this year's handbook and for also designing the front cover
- Caroline Ball and John Cox for their expert editing and proofreading
- Adam Scott, for the photograph on the cover, and to the communications team at Newham University Hospital (part of Barts Health NHS Trust).

We are also grateful to our members and other customers who have provided valuable feedback on previous editions of the handbook/pocket guide, to enable us to make year-on-year improvements.

List of advertisers
BT (inside front cover)
NHS Professionals (back cover)

The author
Peter Davies is a freelance writer and editor. He has written extensively on health policy and management issues, for which he won a major award from the Medical Journalists Association. He was editor of *Health Service Journal* from 1993 to 2002, and has contributed a regular column to *Guardian Unlimited*. He is married with two children and lives in London.